**SCHOLASTIC**

# Traits Writing™

# Student Handbook

## Credits

Cover: bl: © Jeff Greenberg/age fotostock; p. 39 clockwise bl to br: © Opachevsky Irina/Shutterstock, © CABO/Shutterstock, © Slobo/iStockphoto, © Rubén Hidalgo/iStockphoto, © Greenkat/iStockphoto, © Nick M. Do/iStockphoto; p. 47: © Eric Gevaert/Shutterstock; p. 55: © Tomas del Amo/iStockphoto; p. 65: © Ian Tragen/Shutterstock; p. 73: © Muhammet Göktas/iStockphoto; p. 81: © David Earl Crooks/iStockphoto; p. 91: © Hisham Ibrahim/Photoplay/Media Bakery; p. 99: © Popperfoto/Getty Images; p. 107: © TA Cartoons/Shutterstock; p. 117 l: © Liga Alksne/Shutterstock, c: © Bill Noll/iStockphoto, r: © Apollofoto/Shutterstock; p. 125: © Melhi/iStockphoto; p. 133: © Martha Marks/Shutterstock; p. 143: © Jeremy & Claire Weiss/Corbis Outline; p. 151: © Photononstop/SuperStock; p. 159: © Corbis; p. 169: © Ed Bock/Media Bakery; p. 177: © Sergios/Shutterstock; p. 185: © Jeff Greenberg/age fotostock; p. 195: © Jostaphot/iStockphoto; p. 203: James E. Knopf/iStockphoto; p. 211: © Masterfile

Trait Mates Illustration: Wook Jin Jung

Copyright © 2011 by Scholastic Inc.

All rights reserved.      Published by Scholastic Inc.      Printed in the U.S.A.

ISBN-13: 978-0-545-35811-8
ISBN-10: 0-545-35811-6

# Contents

**Week**

# 1

### The Writing Process

**Week**

# 2

### Prewriting

Focus Traits
**Ideas, Organization, and Voice**

**Week**

# 3

### Drafting

Focus Traits
**Word Choice and Sentence Fluency**

**Week**

# 4

### Revising

Focus Traits
**Ideas, Organization, Voice, Word Choice, and Sentence Fluency**

**Week**

# 5

### Editing

Focus Traits
**Conventions and Presentation**

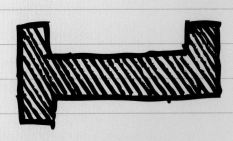

# Getting Started

The writing traits are the language you use with your teacher and classmates to talk about what good writing looks like. The traits are

- **Ideas**
- **Organization**
- **Voice**
- **Word Choice**
- **Sentence Fluency**
- **Conventions**
- **Presentation**

You'll learn more about each trait in the weeks to come. You'll also learn how to use the traits in your own writing as you prewrite, draft, revise, edit, and publish. What makes the traits so great? They help YOU become a great writer!

## Steps in the Writing Process

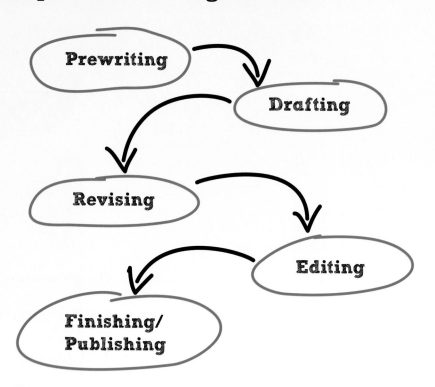

# The Writing Process and the Writing Traits

Think of the writing process as steps that lead to choices you make as a writer. You can spend a lot of time on each one or just a little, and you can follow them in order or go back to one to create a better piece.

When you use the writing process, you talk and think about your writing. That's where the traits come in. The traits are the words and vocabulary you use to describe good writing and how you check your writing to make sure it is the best it can be. The writing process and the traits go together hand in hand.

## The Writing Process and Me

The step in the writing process that will be easiest for me is _____

_____

_____

_____

because _____

_____

_____

_____

The step in the writing process that will be the most challenging for me is _____

_____

because _____

_____

_____

_____

_____

## Meet the Trait Mates

Copy your version of each trait icon in the box and add a short definition of the trait next to it.

All right, writers!
Rev up your pencils.

## The Story Behind My Name

Name _____

How did you get your name?

_____

_____

_____

_____

_____

_____

_____

_____

Illustrate your story here.

## You as a Writer: Taking the Writer's Advice to Heart

**Respond to two of the following items.**

1. Give an example of a book or other written material that taught you something as a writer.

   _____

   _____

   _____

   _____

2. Stop and listen for one minute to what is going on around you. Write down one idea you get from listening that you can use as a writer.

   _____

   _____

   _____

   _____

3. How is practicing writing like practicing a skill such as playing the piano or preparing for a game of soccer or volleyball?

   _____

   _____

   _____

   _____

## My Personal Goals for Writing

What do you hope to accomplish this year?

_____

_____

_____

_____

_____

_____

_____

_____

_____

_____

_____

_____

_____

_____

## Steps in the Writing Process

# Prewriting

When you prewrite, you decide on the purpose and main topic for your writing. You also think about how to organize your ideas and how best to communicate them. Prewriting allows you to explore the possibilities and gives you a place to begin.

# What Writers Think About As They Prewrite

Here are six good techniques for prewriting. Match each technique to an example of what a writer might think about when applying it. Write the number in the blank.

| Prewriting Techniques | Examples |
|---|---|

**1. Reading**
Read books, magazines, and information on the Web.

____ I need to find out about space camp. Maybe I'll call someone at NASA.

**2. Using a Journal**
Record wonderings and experiences.

____ I saw a blue frog at the zoo that was so tiny it could sit in a flower!

**3. Talking**
Discuss topics with other writers, ask questions, and/or contact experts.

____ What if all our wishes came true? That could make a crazy story! Let me write down that idea.

**4. Making a List**
Make a list of writing topics or list details for a topic of your choice.

____ I'm writing a report about J. K. Rowling. Maybe the Scholastic website has some interviews of hers.

**5. Observing**
Watch the world around you or draw on your personal experiences.

____ I heard a woman say her dog ate a whole loaf of bread—plastic and all! That would make a good story.

**6. Listening as a Writer**
Listen to people, places, and things with a "writer's ear."

____ I'm going to list all the invader species I know about—like the Burmese python in the Everglades. Then I'll pick one for my report.

**Ideas are like bananas— there are bunches of them. Pick ones that "a-peel" to you!**

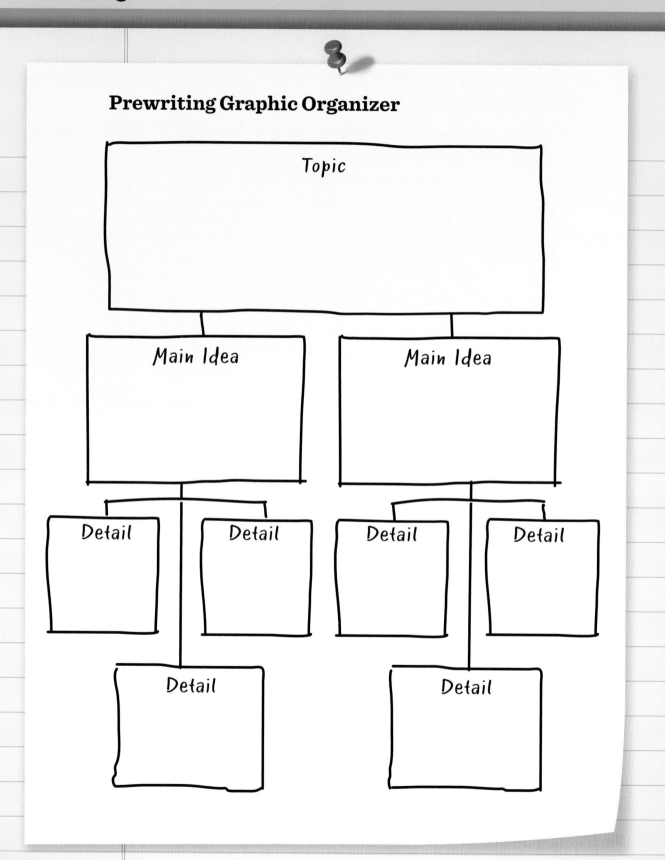

## Prewriting Graphic Organizer

Topic

Main Idea

Main Idea

Detail

Detail

Detail

Detail

Detail

Detail

## My Hero

Who's your hero? Tell us as much as you can about him or her.

_____

_____

_____

_____

_____

_____

_____

_____

_____

_____

_____

_____

_____

_____

Oh, yeah! I'm diving right into this assignment.

## Prewriting Technique Poster Planner

Prewriting Technique: _____

_____

Why this technique can lead to a great draft:

1. _____

_____

_____

2. _____

_____

_____

3. _____

_____

_____

Summary Statement:

_____

_____

_____

_____

_____

# [ Think About: **Prewriting** ]

☐ Did I establish a purpose for my writing and decide on the best way to communicate it?

☐ Did I gather key information about my topic?

☐ Did I consider the audience for my writing, so my choice of voice is appropriate?

☐ Did I make a list, talk to someone, read a book or Web article, write ideas in my journal, observe things around me, listen as a writer, and/or brainstorm about different ideas for writing about this topic?

Here's the big idea ...

... prewriting makes the writing part a lot easier!

Ideas

Organization

## Steps in the Writing Process

# Drafting

You've come up with some original and intriguing ideas in prewriting. Now it's time to start drafting. When you draft, you get your ideas down in rough form and think about the organization. You put pencil to paper and let your ideas flow, not worrying about spelling or other conventions.

# What Writers Think About As They Draft

Writers draft to get ideas down on paper. They might create a lead, sketch the main ideas, add an ending, and play with voice. Of course, they think about word choice and sentence fluency—but those are worked on during revision. Conventions can be saved for the editing stage.

> ### The blue whale
>
> Can you name the biggest animal. Not the elephant. The blue whale. It's huge. It can waigh 200 tons. Its heart can waigh over 1,000 pound. That's a lot of whale
>
> What does it eat? It eats tiny creechurs called krill. Thousands and thousands of them.
>
> blue whales lives in all Oceans. They make noises other blue whales can here. You should read about the blue whale.

Nothing wrong with a "ruff" start!

You can smooth things out later.

## What Slows Me Down When I Draft

When I draft, some of the things that slow me down are _____

_____

_____

_____

_____

_____

my spelling

knowing how to begin

whether I've used enough strong verbs

whether I've found the best way to say something

whether I've said enough

where I should speed up or slow down

whether I have enough information

how to end

my punctuation

if I'm being interesting

whether my sentences begin too much the same way

giving my reader what he or she needs to know

# See How the Language Changes!

The Declaration of Independence changed the world. But it contains a lot of words we don't use today. Match the original words of the document to the simplified, updated ones. Write the letter in the blank space.

## Original Words

1. When in the course of human events: ____

2. it becomes necessary for one people to dissolve the political bands which have connected them with another: ____

3. and to assume among the powers of the earth: ____

4. the separate and equal station to which the Laws of Nature and of Nature's God entitle them: ____

5. a decent respect to the opinions of mankind: ____

6. requires that they should declare the causes which impel them to the separation: ____

## Simplified, Updated Words

**A.** *a basic sense of right and wrong should guide you*

**B.** *As time goes by and things happen,*

**C.** *to give those people clear reasons for why you are making the break. It's only fair.*

**D.** *—out of respect for those involved and even if they don't agree with you—*

**E.** *and begin to act on your own,*

**F.** *if you must break a tie with people you have had a connection with*

Who chose those words?!
I declare ...
I have a headache!

## Freedom and Democracy: A 35-Word Sentence

Write a 35-word sentence on what freedom and democracy mean to you.

_____ _____ _____ _____ _____ (5)

_____ _____ _____ _____ _____ (10)

_____ _____ _____ _____ _____ (15)

_____ _____ _____ _____ _____ (20)

_____ _____ _____ _____ _____ (25)

_____ _____ _____ _____ _____ (30)

_____ _____ _____ _____ _____ (35)

# [ Think About: **Drafting** ]

- ☐ Did I use my prewriting notes to capture the most important points?

- ☐ Did I let the power of my idea drive my drafting decisions?

- ☐ Did I just write, without worrying about making the piece perfect?

- ☐ Did I get down key words, phrases, and sentences, knowing I can revise them for accuracy later?

## My Five-Word Sentence

**Revise the 35-word sentence you drafted by reducing it to only five words.**

_____  _____  _____

_____  _____

Have you lost some words?

I have! Can you tell?

Wow! Working out much?

Presentation

Voice

## Steps in the Writing Process

Prewriting

Drafting

Revising

Editing

Finishing/
Publishing

# Revising

When you revise, you make changes to your draft so it can be as clear as it can be. You reread and rework your piece until it is just right for the reader. Save any worries about conventions until the editing stage. Revising often begins with sharing your writing with someone else. Then you can use the traits to polish it up and make it shine!

# What Writers Think About As They Revise

**Here are some questions you can ask yourself when you revise.**

## Ideas
- Is my topic focused and developed?
- Are my details interesting and correct?
- Did I include some new thinking about my topic?

## Organization
- Do my details unfold in order?
- Does the organization make reading my piece a breeze?

## Voice
- Does my voice give my piece a "personal stamp"?
- Do I have my audience and purpose clearly in mind?
- Do I present ideas in an original way?

## Word Choice
- Are my words clear and correct? Do they sound natural?
- Do my words show that I have a powerful vocabulary?

## Sentence Fluency
- Have I written a variety of well-built sentences?
- Have I woven my sentences together to create a smooth-sounding piece?

Your draft's a little weak? A revision will help. Let's pump it up!

Organization

## Revision at Work

Writers revise—and so do people in other jobs. Think about how, and finish the sentences.

*Writers revise and so do . . .*

1. cooks when they _____

2. chemists when they _____

3. artists when they _____

4. comedians when they _____

5. musicians when they _____

~~Kim~~
~~she~~
~~Girl~~
student

**Writers revise, and so do ducks when they...**

**Quack on and on and on and on!**

Voice

Conventions

## My Funny Experience

Everyone has humorous moments. Write about one of yours.

_____

_____

_____

_____

_____

_____

_____

_____

_____

_____

_____

_____

_____

_____

_____

_____

_____

_____

# Revising

## Authors and Artists Revise

How are Lisa Yee and Theo van Doesburg's revision processes similar and different?

| Similar | Different |
| --- | --- |
| | |
| | |
| | |
| | |
| | |
| | |
| | |
| | |
| | |
| | |
| | |

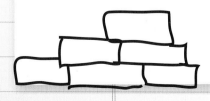

# [ Think About: **Revising** ]

☐ Did I zero in on a small part of my big idea?

☐ Did I anticipate and answer the reader's questions?

☐ Did I refine the words and sentences so they are clear?

☐ Did I start out strong and end just as strong?

## Steps in the Writing Process

Prewriting → Drafting → Revising → Editing → Finishing/Publishing

# Editing

You edit so that others can easily read what you've written. When you edit, you check your work for spelling, capitalization, punctuation and paragraphing, and grammar and usage. You clean up your writing to follow standard rules of English. Editing can improve your work in other traits, too. Watch—you'll see this come true!

# What Writers Think About As They Edit

Conventions are the "rules of the writing road." They guide the reader through your piece by making it easy to read. Here are some questions about conventions to ask yourself as you edit.

## Spelling
- Did I spell words correctly—even the hard ones?

## Capitalization
- Did I use capital letters correctly, even in tricky places?

## Punctuation and Paragraphing
- Did I use punctuation correctly—or purposely use punctuation creatively?
- Did I begin paragraphs in all the right places?

## Grammar and Usage
- Did I follow grammar and usage rules to make my writing clear and readable?

## What Needs to Be Corrected?

Find a partner and circle the errors in this piece.

### The blue whale

Can you name the biggest animal on earth. No, its not the elephant. The biggest animal is the blue whale.

Just how big is a blue whale? A blue whale are huge. It can waigh as much 200 tons. It's heart can waigh over 1,000 pound. that's a lot of whale

What does a blue whale eat? You might think it eats really big things. But it doesnt. A blue whale eats tiny shrimp-like creechurs called krill. It takes thousands and thousands of krill to feed a hungry blue whale.

blue whales lives in all the Oceans. They make noises that other blue whales can here for miles and miles. If you want to learn more about a interesting animal, read about the blue whale.

# [ Think About: **Editing** ]

☐ Did I check my spelling one word at a time?

☐ Did I add punctuation and paragraphing where it's needed?

☐ Did I use capital letters correctly?

☐ Did I apply standard English grammar and usage?

Spelling. Check.
Punctuation. Check.
Capital letters. Check.
Standard English.
Oh yeah!

# Editing

## Tips for Editing on a Computer

### Tools I Can Use to Edit for Conventions

| | |
|---|---|
| insert | Use to add letters, words, phrases, or sentences. |
| delete | Remove unwanted letters, words, phrases, or sentences. |
| find and replace | Search for and replace a specific word or phrase. |
| cut, copy, and paste | Highlight text to cut or copy and paste elsewhere. |
| undo | Undo typing and return to your previous version. |
| check spelling | Turn on the spell check, so misspelled words will be underlined in red. Check possible substitutions. |

### Tools I Can Use to Edit for Presentation

| | |
|---|---|
| change font | Want your piece to stand out? Select the best, most readable font for your document. You can even choose a fancy font for your title. |
| change style (boldface, underline, italic, size, case, bullets) | It's fun to <u>underline</u> text or make it **bold** or *italic*. You can also change the size of a word or make lowercase letters all UPPERCASE. Use bullets to make lists easier to read. |
| change color | WOW! You can really make words pop or call attention to them by using color. |
| change line spacing | Text too heavy to read? Change the spacing between the lines to help out. |
| insert art or graphics | Need to add a picture or chart? Use clip art or your own pictures to jazz up your piece! |

**What's black and white and read all over? A good-looking piece of writing!**

Presentation

## Rate the Papers

Here are two examples of expository writing.
Which paper is stronger? Why do you think so?

### Paper 1

Quill pens are messy. You have to fill them up with ink. I don't know who invented them but they are not very good. A ballpoint pen is a lot easier to use. Quill pens look cool, but they are not so cool to write with. I wouldn't want to write with one for very long. It would make me tired of writing.

### Paper 2

If I lived back in the 1800s, I would not have wanted to write a long assignment. You would have to use a quill or even a steel pen! In order to write you would have to keep dipping your quill or pen in the ink. I thought using a pencil was hard! Imagine how many times you would go to dip your pen and you would smudge your writing. It would look so messy when you were done. Thank goodness I live now.

# Editing

## Editing Marks

| Mark | Meaning | Example |
|------|---------|---------|
| ℘ | Delete material. | The writing is is good. |
| sp | Correct the spelling or spell it out. | We are exploring ② traits this weak. |
| ◯ | Close space. | To day is publishing day. |
| ∧ | Insert a letter, word, or phrase. | My teacher has books. wonderful |
| ℘ | Change a letter. | She is a great wroter. |
| ⧢ | Add a space. | Don't forget astrong lead. |
| ∿ | Transpose letters or words. | She raed the piece with flair! |
| ≡ | Change to a capital letter. | We have j. k. Rowling to thank for Harry Potter's magic. |
| / | Change to a lowercase letter. | "A Writer's work is never Done" was his favorite saying. |
| ¶ | Start a new paragraph. | "What day is it?" he inquired. "It's National Writing Day," she replied. |
| ⊙ | Add a period. | Think about all the traits as you write ⊙ |

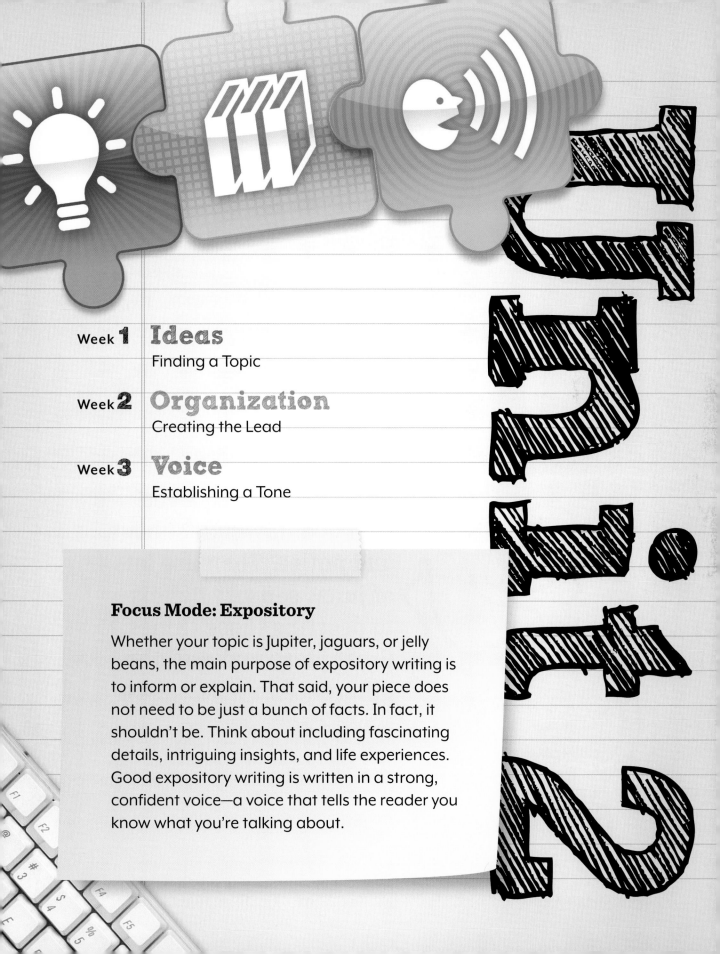

### Focus Mode: Expository

Whether your topic is Jupiter, jaguars, or jelly beans, the main purpose of expository writing is to inform or explain. That said, your piece does not need to be just a bunch of facts. In fact, it shouldn't be. Think about including fascinating details, intriguing insights, and life experiences. Good expository writing is written in a strong, confident voice—a voice that tells the reader you know what you're talking about.

- **Finding a Topic** .........................
- Focusing the Topic
- Developing the Topic
- Using Details

**Focus Mode: Expository**

# Ideas

**❝ Write about things you care about, wonder about, and notice. Then use lots of juicy, sensory details to describe those things. Great ideas make all the difference in writing! ❞**

# Finding a Topic

Topics are all around you—in things you experience every day. When you find the perfect topic, you know what to say. You see the "big picture." To find the perfect topic, think about what matters to you and let your ideas soar.

**How is collecting things that matter to you like searching for good writing topics?**

# Picturing Topics

One way to collect ideas for writing is through pictures. Use photos and drawings to stir your imagination and reveal topics that are meaningful.

1. Collect photos and drawings that capture your attention—from magazines, newspapers, family albums, and other sources around you.

2. Study each picture. Jot down what you notice, wonder, and feel about one of them.

3. What information does the picture contain? Write a caption to get started.

| What I Notice | What I Wonder | What I Feel |
|---|---|---|
|  |  |  |

Caption: _____

# Warm-Up 1

**Is there an idea in here? Hello? Hello?**

**How clear is this paragraph's topic?**

There are many different types of homes for animals. Animals need food, water, and shelter. Building or finding a home is hard work for an animal in the wild.

**Revise the paragraph here or on a separate sheet.**

## Think About

- Have I chosen a topic I really like?
- Do I have something new to say about this topic?
- Am I writing about what I know and care about?
- Have I gathered enough information so that I'm ready to write?

**Preview**

# Betsy Franco, author of *Zero Is the Leaves on the Tree*

**Read the information about Betsy Franco below and answer two of the questions.**

When Betsy Franco was in college, she studied acting—and she is taking acting classes again! She says that acting helps her with her writing. She writes picture books, poetry, novels, and nonfiction. So far, she has published more than 80 books. One thing she loves to do through her writing is show her readers how creative and exciting math can be.

1. Betsy Franco has had passions for acting and writing her whole life. Do you think it's important to have passions? Why? What are yours?

_____

_____

_____

2. How do you think taking part in acting classes may have helped Betsy Franco with her writing?

_____

_____

_____

_____

3. What do you think you might learn from *Zero Is the Leaves on the Tree*? Why do you think the author chose this title for her book?

_____

_____

_____

# Write-On Sheet

## [ Focus on Punctuation ]

Write two sentences that show the correct use of colons.

1.

2.

> **❝** If you're going to be a writer, the first essential is just to write. Do not wait for an idea. Start writing something and the ideas will come. You have to turn the faucet on before the water starts to flow. **❞**
>
> —Louis L'Amour

# [ Zero Web ]

Write three examples of zero from *Zero Is the Leaves on the Tree*.
Then write three of your own examples.

**Betsy Franco's Examples**

ZERO

**My Examples**

Zero ideas?
No way!

- **Creating the Lead** ...........................
- Using Sequence Words and Transition Words
- Structuring the Body
- Ending With a Sense of Resolution

**Focus Mode: Expository**

# Organization

**❝Organization is about the structure of a piece of writing. Nothing holds your piece together—or holds a reader's attention— better than sturdy, easy-to-follow organization. ❞**

# Creating the Lead

The lead is the beginning of a piece of writing—its first lines. A strong lead grabs the reader's attention. It gives the reader something to think about so that he or she wants to keep reading to find out what you have to say.

**How is being first in a race similar to having a really strong lead in a piece of writing?**

# A Strong Start

A strong start leads readers into your writing. Here are six techniques for creating one.

### Single Word

The writer sets off an important word by itself and follows it up with more information.

**Example:**

Gum. Gum was everywhere. It was in my hair. It was in the carpet. It was on my pillow.

### Fascinating Fact

The writer presents an intriguing piece of information.

**Example:**

I blew a bubble bigger than my brother's head.

### Imagine This

The writer captures a moment in words or pictures.

**Example:**

The gum made my bangs stick straight out from my head.

### Compare It

The writer provides different ways of looking at the topic.

**Example:**

Sugar-free gum may be better for me, but I can blow bigger bubbles with regular gum.

### Listen Up

The writer describes a sound.

**Example:**

Smack, snap, slurp!

### I Wonder

The writer asks a question or a series of questions.

**Example:**

Have you ever wondered how many pieces of gum will fit into the human mouth? Five? Ten? More?

# Warm-Up 2

**This paragraph is begging to fly. Give it some wings!**

**How strong is the lead in this paragraph?**

I'm going to tell you about baby birds. You might see them on the ground. Some baby birds are older fledglings. They are learning how to fly.

**Revise the paragraph here or on a separate sheet.**

Organization

## Think About

- Have I given the reader something interesting to think about right from the start?

- Will the reader want to keep reading?

- Have I tried to get the reader's attention?

- Have I let the reader know what is coming?

**Preview**

# A Journalist

In the spaces below, write about what you think a journalist does, how changes in communication affect a journalist's work, and thoughts you have about the job.

1. A journalist does not just keep a journal! Here is what I think a journalist does:

_____

_____

_____

_____

2. The Internet has affected the job of a journalist. Here are some ways that being a journalist might be different now from the way it used to be:

_____

_____

_____

_____

3. What I think must be most challenging about the job:

_____

_____

_____

_____

# Write-On Sheet

# [ My Spelling Words ]

List your nine spelling words for the week here.

1.

2.

3.

4.

5.

6.

7.

8.

9.

> 66 You don't have to be great to get started, but you have to get started to be great. 99
>
> –Les Brown

# [ The Most Fascinating Creature of Them All ]

Did you write a bold BIGFOOT beginning? Oh, I see, not YETI!

**Pick one of these mythological creatures and research it.**

- **Loch Ness Monster** is a sea creature that lives in a Scottish lake.
- **The Yeti** is a Bigfoot-like creature from the mountains of Nepal and Northern Tibet.
- **The Lusca** is a sea monster that lives in the Caribbean.
- **The Mokele-mbembe** is a living dinosaur from the jungles of the central African countries of Congo, Cameroon, and Gabon.
- **The Kongamato** is a beaked, flying creature from deep in the African bush.

**Name the creature you chose and list five interesting facts about it.**

**My Creature:** _____

**Facts**

1. _____
2. _____
3. _____
4. _____
5. _____

**Write the lead for a short article about this creature. Try to capture the reader's interest so he or she will want to read more. Share your lead with a classmate and revise it to make it even stronger.**

_____

_____

_____

**Write an outline for the rest of your article on a separate sheet of paper. Include as many facts as you can.**

- **Establishing a Tone** ••••••••••••••••••••••••••••••••••••••
- Conveying the Purpose
- Creating a Connection to the Audience
- Taking Risks to Create Voice

**Focus Mode: Expository**

# Voice

Voice

**66** Voice is how you speak to readers. It's how you connect to them and show how much you care about your main idea, whether you're writing fiction or nonfiction. It's the energy in your writing. **99**

# Establishing a Tone

When you talk, you express how you feel by your body language and the sound, or tone, of your voice. When you write, you express how you feel by the tone of the words you choose. The right tone lets readers know how you feel about the topic and how you want them to feel about it.

**How is painting with your own style like finding the tone of a piece of writing?**

# Set the Tone

The tone of your writing is the emotion or attitude you express. It can vary depending on your audience and purpose. Here are some examples.

| | | |
|---|---|---|
| happy | playful | mean |
| angry | entertaining | excited |
| relaxed | inquisitive | frustrated |
| funny | knowledgeable | scared |
| friendly | serious | sad |
| worried | gentle | thoughtful |
| cautious | determined | annoyed |
| soothing | silly | bored |
| nervous | convincing | confident |

**Read each sentence and write down words that match its tone.**

1. She stormed into her room and slammed the door.

   _____

2. She tiptoed into her room and gently closed the door.

   _____

3. She tiptoed into her room and quickly closed the door.

   _____

4. She strolled into her room and casually closed the door.

   _____

5. She skipped into her room and twirled as she closed the door.

   _____

## Explore More

You can detect tone not only in writing, but in music, art, drama, and dance. Listen to your favorite song. Can you identify its tone? Does it remain the same throughout?

# Warm-Up 3

This paragraph is low on fuel. Fill 'er up and make 'er soar.

**How is the tone of this paragraph?**

The Wright brothers flew the first powered airplane on December 17, 1903. There were other inventors before them. Thomas Moy invented the Aerial Steamer. Clement Ader invented the Bat Plane. Jean-Marie Le Bris invented the Artificial Albatross. Leonardo da Vinci designed the Ornithopter.

**Revise the paragraph here or on a separate sheet.**

## Think About

• Can I name the primary voice of my writing (for example: happy, upset, wise, scared)?

• Have I changed the tone from the beginning to the end?

• Have I shown how I feel?

• Did I show that I care about this topic?

**Preview**
# Molly Bang and Penny Chisholm,
**authors of *Living Sunlight***

**Find a partner, discuss the questions below, and answer two of them.**

1. *Living Sunlight* explains how plants convert sunlight into a form of energy they—and we—can use. The authors tell the story from the point of view of the sun. How do you think this helped them establish a tone?

_____

_____

_____

_____

2. Molly Bang has written and illustrated many kinds of picture books. Penny Chisholm is a scientist who studies plants. How do you think they combined their skills and knowledge to create this book?

_____

_____

_____

_____

3. Molly Bang says one of her goals as an author is to share her fascination with science. Some of her topics include photosynthesis, solar energy, and environmental protection. What topic do you think she should write about next?

_____

_____

_____

_____

# Write-On Sheet

# [ Focus on Capitalization ]

Write two sentences that contain correct use of capitalization after colons.

1.

2.

> **"** Be yourself. Above all, let who you are, what you are, what you believe shine through every sentence you write, every piece you finish. **"**
>
> —John Jakes

# [ Tone Triangle ]

How do Molly Bang and Penny Chisholm express their feelings, attitudes, and knowledge about plants in *Living Sunlight*? Fill in information about the passage you heard.

What did the curve say to the angle when she couldn't finish her graphic organizer?

*Tri*angle, try!

**Overall Tone
of the Passage**

_____

**Sentences from the Passage
That Capture the Tone**

1. _____

_____

2. _____

_____

3. _____

_____

# [ Expository Publishing Checklist ]

Think you are ready to go public with your expository unit project? Use this form to make sure you've covered all the writing bases.

Check. Check. Quack. Check. Check.

I remembered to

☐ include facts and information that came from reliable sources.

☐ weave in details that show how much I know about my topic.

☐ develop the topic logically from beginning to end.

☐ use a voice that expresses my fascination for the topic.

☐ explain any unusual words, phrases, or concepts.

☐ read my piece aloud to check how it will sound to the readers.

☐ proofread my piece carefully and clean up problems with conventions.

The purpose of my piece is

_____

The part that works best is

_____

What I hope readers will take away from my piece is

_____

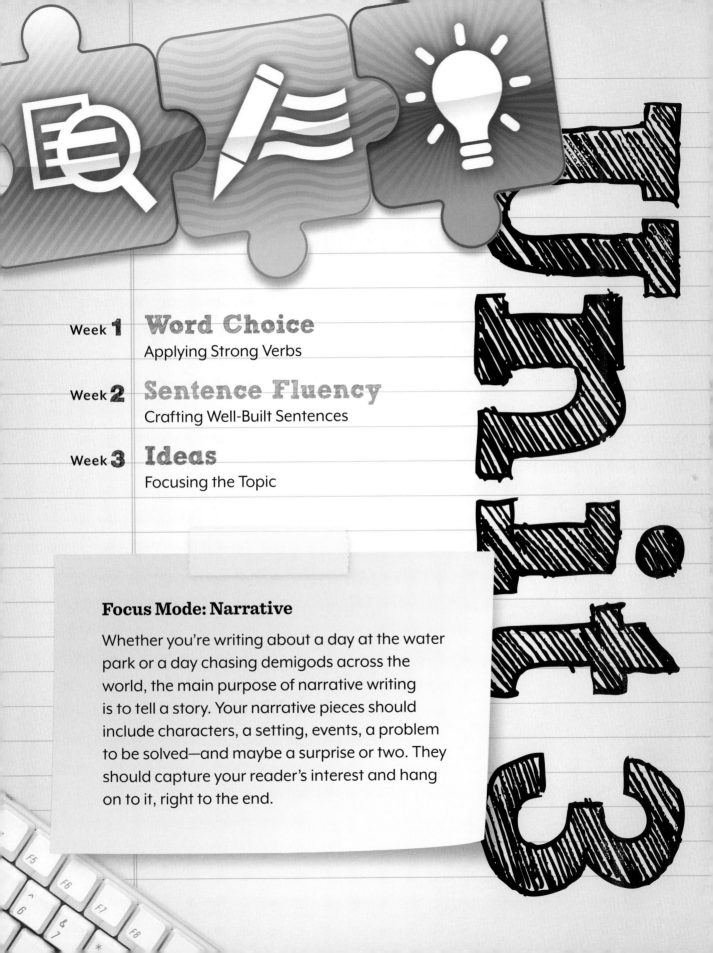

**UNIT 3**

### Focus Mode: Narrative

Whether you're writing about a day at the water park or a day chasing demigods across the world, the main purpose of narrative writing is to tell a story. Your narrative pieces should include characters, a setting, events, a problem to be solved—and maybe a surprise or two. They should capture your reader's interest and hang on to it, right to the end.

- **Applying Strong Verbs** ·······························
- Selecting Striking Words and Phrases
- Using Specific and Accurate Words
- Choosing Words That Deepen Meaning

**Focus Mode: Narrative**

# Word Choice

Word Choice

**"Using the right words allows you to show what is happening in your piece or what matters to you about your topic. Precise and accurate words help make your main idea stand out."**

# Applying Strong Verbs

You can kick a soccer ball or you can *boot* a soccer ball. You can sit down on the sofa or you can *plop* on the sofa. Which would you rather do? Strong verbs pack a punch. They capture action precisely in just one word. When you use strong verbs, your writing comes alive. It bursts with action and color!

**How is choosing the right verb similar to enlivening your picture with exactly the color you imagined?**

# Choosing Vivid Verbs

Vivid verbs help paint a picture in your reader's mind. Here are three tips for choosing them.

**Picture It!** Close your eyes and run the movie of your story in your mind. What are your characters doing? Choose verbs that capture it.

- I <u>spoke to</u> my mom about the field trip.
- Lisa <u>ran by</u> the other team's best player.

**Stretch Those Verbs!** Picture the action and dig deeper for a better verb.

- I <u>reminded</u> my mom about the field trip.
- I <u>complained to</u> my mom about the field trip.
- Lisa <u>exploded past</u> the other team's best player.
- Lisa <u>thundered past</u> the other team's best player.

**Get Active!** Keep your sentences active, not passive. Have the subject do the action. Avoid too many sentences that contain forms of the verb *to be* (e.g., *is, am, are, was, were, be, being, been*). Show what the subject does, not what it is.

| Passive Sentences | Active Sentences |
|---|---|
| • The toad <u>was hidden</u> by the leaves. | • The toad <u>hid</u> among the leaves. |
| • The leaves <u>were</u> on top of the toad. | • The leaves <u>disguised</u> the toad. |
| | • The toad <u>nestled</u> in the leaves. |

# Warm-Up 4

You want stormy verbs?
I crush. I destroy. I pul-ver-ize!

**How are the verbs in this paragraph?**

The tornado was very close to my house. It was windy and loud. It made me nervous. I was scared.

**Revise the paragraph here or on a separate sheet.**

## Think About

- Have I used action words?
- Did I stretch to get a better word—*scurry* rather than *run?*
- Do my verbs give my writing punch and pizzazz?
- Did I avoid *is, am, are, was, were, be, being,* and *been* whenever I could?

**Preview**

# Nick Bruel, author of *Bad Kitty*

Find a partner, discuss the questions below, and answer
two of them.

**1.** Nick Bruel is a cartoonist as well as a writer. How do you think being skilled at
drawing and writing affects the way he develops his books?

_____

_____

_____

_____

**2.** Nick Bruel has written several books featuring the same cat. If you were going to
write a funny pet story, what kind of animal would you choose as your subject?
Why?

_____

_____

_____

_____

**3.** After reading *Bad Kitty*, some kids decided to create their own book called "Bad
Kiddies" about a kindergarten class that misbehaves. What are some strong
verbs the kids may have used to make the story fun to read?

_____

_____

_____

_____

# Write-On Sheet

# [ My Spelling Words ]

List your nine spelling words for the week here.

1.
2.
3.
4.
5.
6.
7.
8.
9.

> 66 The difference between the right word and the almost-right word is the difference between lightning and a lightning bug. 99
>
> —Mark Twain

# [ *Bad Kitty Graphic Organizer* ]

Look for the strong verbs Nick Bruel uses to describe the actions of the bad kitty and the good kitty. For each kitty, write three strong verbs and three matching ordinary verbs.

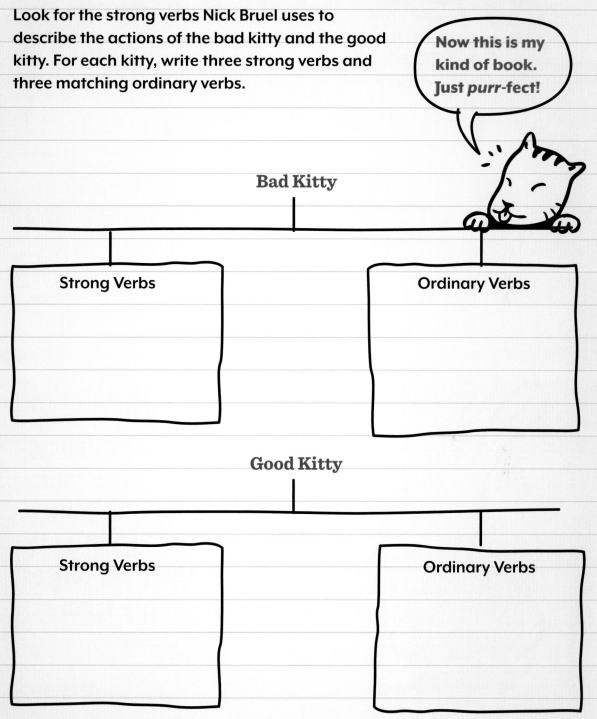

Now this is my kind of book. Just *purr*-fect!

**Bad Kitty**

Strong Verbs

Ordinary Verbs

**Good Kitty**

Strong Verbs

Ordinary Verbs

- **Crafting Well-Built Sentences** ·················
- Varying Sentence Types
- Capturing Smooth and Rhythmic Flow
- Breaking the "Rules" to Create Fluency

**Focus Mode: Narrative**

# Sentence Fluency

Sentence Fluency

**❝To create sentence fluency, you have to read with your ears *and* eyes. Make your writing sound as good as it looks by building sentences that flow smoothly from one to the next.❞**

# Crafting Well-Built Sentences

What does it mean for a piece of writing to have well-built sentences? It means the sentences are not all short or all long. They start with different words, not the same word over and over again. Words like *but, and,* and *so* join sentence parts. Well-built sentences are carefully crafted and are a breeze to read.

**How is transforming lumber into furniture like crafting well-built sentences?**

# Rock-Solid Sentences

Read these two versions of the same passage.

| Passage 1 | Passage 2 |
|---|---|
| We went to the beach. It was sunny. It was warm. We flew kites. We ate hot dogs. Had fun. | We spent a warm, sunny day at the beach. While there, we flew kites and ate hot dogs. What fun we had! |

Fill in the chart for each passage by recording the number of words in each sentence and then writing down the first two.

## Passage 1

| Sentence Number | Number of Words | First Words |
|---|---|---|
| 1 | 5 | We went |
| 2 | | |
| 3 | | |
| 4 | | |
| 5 | | |
| 6 | | |

## Passage 2

| Sentence Number | Number of Words | First Words |
|---|---|---|
| 1 | | |
| 2 | | |
| 3 | | |

**What did the writer of Passage 2 do to craft well-built sentences?**

☐ made sure all the sentences didn't begin in the same way

☐ made some sentences long and others short

☐ combined sentences using *and*

☐ checked grammar so that all sentences were correct

# Warm-Up 5

Are the sentences in this paragraph well built?

I have the flu. I felt terrible. I can't sleep. I'm restless. Grouchy me! I'm not a good patient. I wish I could rest. I hate the flu.

Revise the paragraph here or on a separate sheet.

**Have no fear. The Fluency Doctor is here!**

Sentence Fluency

## Think About

- Do my sentences begin in different ways?

- Are my sentences of different lengths?

- Are my sentences grammatically correct unless I broke rules for impact?

- Have I used conjunctions such as *but, and,* and *so* to connect parts of sentences?

**Preview**

# A Travel Writer

In the spaces below, write your thoughts about what a travel writer does, where you might find a travel writer's work, and questions you have about the job.

1. A travel writer must be on the move a lot of the time. What I think a travel writer does before writing:

_____

_____

_____

_____

_____

2. Where I have seen—or might see—the work of a travel writer:

_____

_____

_____

_____

_____

3. What I wonder about how a travel writer decides what to tell readers:

_____

_____

_____

_____

_____

# Write-On Sheet

# [ Focus on Grammar and Usage ]

Write two sentences that contain adverbs used correctly.

1. _____

_____

_____

2. _____

_____

_____

_____

> 66 All the words I use in my stories can be found in the dictionary—it's just a matter of arranging them into the right sentences. 99
>
> —W. Somerset Maugham

# [ Not-So-Ordinary Travel Destination ]

Pick one of these not-so-ordinary travel destinations and research it for a field review in a travel guide.

- **Congress Avenue Bridge Bats,** Austin, Texas
- **Corn Palace,** Mitchell, South Dakota
- **Lucy the Elephant,** Margate, New Jersey
- **Odor-Eaters Rotten Sneaker Contest,** Montpelier, Vermont
- **Watermelon Water Tower and Watermelon Thump,** Luling, Texas

A rotten sneaker contest? Dude, that stinks!

Sentence Fluency

1. Let's visit

   _____

   _____

2. This destination is not so ordinary because

   _____

   _____

3. The short story behind this not-so-ordinary destination is

   _____

   _____

4. Travelers should also know

   _____

   _____

**On a separate sheet of paper, write a field review that will make readers want to travel to your destination. Include websites, photos, and a map.**

- Finding a Topic
- **Focusing the Topic** ....................
- Developing the Topic
- Using Details

**Focus Mode: Narrative**

# Ideas

66 **Write about things you care about, wonder about, and notice. Then use lots of juicy, sensory details to describe those things. Great ideas make all the difference in writing!** 99

# Focusing the Topic

When you focus your topic, you zero in on something important or interesting about it. You make your writing clear and strong because you're not taking on the whole world—you're just taking on one really cool corner of it.

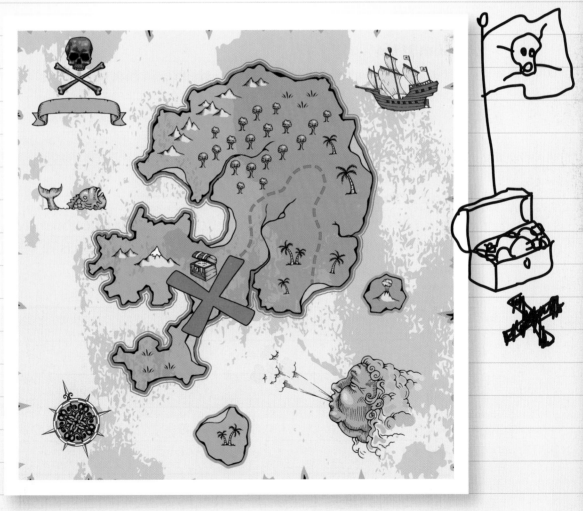

**How is pinpointing a specific location on a map like focusing a writing topic?**

**Ideas: Focusing the Topic**

# Narrow That Topic

**Writers must keep their ideas focused in order to keep readers' attention. Follow these steps to narrow the topic "my vacation."**

### 1. Narrow It Down

"My vacation" is too broad. So narrow it by focusing on one specific moment that sticks out in your mind. Ask yourself: *What do I see when I close my eyes and picture this vacation?*

Narrow it: _____

Narrow it more: _____

Narrow it even more: _____

### 2. Sum It Up

If your topic is focused, you can sum it up in one sentence. Write a summary sentence here.

_____

_____

### 3. Add It In or Cut It Out

What information will you share? Too much information may bore readers. Too little may confuse them. Write + for details to keep and − for details to cut.

☐ _____

☐ _____

☐ _____

☐ _____

☐ _____

☐ _____

☐ _____

# Warm-Up 6

**I know there's a great idea in here...** *somewhere.*

**Is this paragraph's topic focused?**

It can be scary to be left on your own. I'm eleven and my parents leave me home sometimes when they go to the movies. My brothers and sisters don't mind being alone in the house.

**Revise the paragraph here or on a separate sheet.**

## Think About

- Have I zeroed in on one small part of a bigger idea?
- Can I sum up my idea in a simple sentence?
- Have I chosen the information that captures my idea best?
- Have I thought deeply about what the reader will need to know?

## Ideas: **Focusing the Topic**

# Margaret Peterson Haddix,

**author of** *Dexter the Tough*

Find a partner, discuss the questions below, and answer two of them.

1. Margaret Peterson Haddix used to be a reporter. Writing factual stories led her to think of characters and plots for fictional stories. So she started writing novels for kids. Do you prefer writing fiction or nonfiction? Why?

_____

_____

_____

_____

2. When she was writing *Dexter the Tough*, Haddix imagined that Dexter was telling his story to her. How might imagining a character as a real person help you focus your topic and bring it to life?

_____

_____

_____

_____

3. What do you think *Dexter the Tough* will be about? What does being "tough" mean to you?

_____

_____

_____

_____

# Write-On Sheet

# [ My Spelling Words ]

List your nine spelling words for the week here.

1.

2.

3.

4.

5.

6.

7.

8.

9.

> ❝ I didn't have time to write a short letter, so I wrote a long one instead. ❞
>
> —**Blaise Pascal**

# [ *Dexter the Tough* Graphic Organizer ]

Dexter and Robin had very different ideas about their friendship. Write down their ideas and three details from the book that support those ideas.

OUCH! Get off of my de*tail*!

## Dexter's Idea

Details:

- 
- 
- 

## Robin's Idea

Details:

- 
- 
-

# [ Narrative Publishing Checklist ]

Think you are ready to go public with your narrative unit project? Use this form to make sure you've covered all the writing bases.

My favorite part is... handing it in!

**I remembered to**

☐ develop a fascinating story line with interesting characters.

☐ include a time and a place that work well with the story line.

☐ present a problem and a solution.

☐ give the story a clear beginning, middle, and end.

☐ use an active voice to entertain, surprise, and challenge the reader.

☐ choose words that enhance the characters, time, and place.

☐ read my piece aloud to check for how it will sound to readers.

☐ proofread my piece carefully and clean up problems with conventions.

Presentation

The purpose of my piece is

_____

My favorite part is

_____

What I hope readers will find most memorable about my piece is

_____

### Focus Mode: Persuasive

Whether you're asking your parents to buy your favorite cereal or nominating your best friend for class president, the main purpose of persuasive writing is to construct an argument. Your piece should clearly state a position and stick with that position. You need to offer good, sound reasoning, and use a strong, confident voice to let your reader know you mean business.

- Creating the Lead
- **Using Sequence Words and Transition Words** ......................................
- Structuring the Body
- Ending With a Sense of Resolution

**Focus Mode: Persuasive**

# Organization

Organization

**66 Organization is about the structure of a piece of writing. Nothing holds your piece together—or holds a reader's attention—better than sturdy, easy-to-follow organization. 99**

# Using Sequence Words and Transition Words

Sequence words (like *next* and *finally*) and transition words (like *but* and *also*) are the "linking words" you use to connect your ideas from one sentence to the next. When you use the right words, your sentences fit together perfectly—like bricks in a wall.

How is using sequence words and transition words like strengthening a brick wall with mortar?

# Connect It!

Sequence and transition words link ideas. Here are some words you can use.

| Time Sequence | Location |
|---|---|
| first, second, third, last, then, next, after, earlier, before, now, soon, later, last night, yesterday, today, tomorrow, this morning, simultaneously, at the same time, meanwhile, followed by, all night, finally | above, below, next to, behind, in front of, in back of, over, under, on top, on the bottom, alongside, outside, inside, nearby, beyond, across, around, between, at the end |
| **Compare or Contrast** | **Added Information** |
| similarly, likewise, in the same way, equally, as well as, by comparison, generally, usually, best of all, in contrast, conversely, instead of, although, even though, except, but, however, on the other hand | also, for example, for instance, in addition, to clarify, yet, another, besides that, because, including, such as, furthermore, in other words, which, not only, one more thing |
| **Emphasis** | **Summary** |
| certainly, clearly, especially, unfortunately, absolutely, above all, without question, without a doubt, in fact, most important | finally, therefore, as a result, so, for the most part, for these reasons, in conclusion, to summarize, thus, consequently, in short, in the end |

Write six pairs of sentences, below or on a separate sheet. In each pair, use a sequence or transition word from the boxes above  (Example: "I thought she was going to play her guitar **all night**. **Finally**, she stopped at midnight.")

1. _____

2. _____

3. _____

4. _____

5. _____

6. _____

# Warm-Up 7

This is "some paragraph." Make like Charlotte and put a new spin on it?

**How are the sequence and transition words in this paragraph?**

I think Charlotte from Charlotte's Web is amazing! She wrote words in her web to help Wilbur. She wrote "Some Pig." She wrote "Terrific." She wrote "Radiant." She wrote "Humble." Her words saved Wilbur's life. She should get an award.

**Revise the paragraph here or on a separate sheet.**

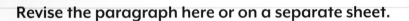

## Think About

- Have I used sequence words such as *later, then,* and *meanwhile*?

- Did I use a variety of transition words such as *however, because, also,* and *for instance*?

- Have I shown how the ideas connect from sentence to sentence?

- Does my organization make sense from paragraph to paragraph?

**Preview**

# Loreen Leedy, author of *The Shocking Truth About Energy*

**Find a partner, discuss the questions below, and answer two of them.**

**1.** There are lots of books about electricity and energy. One thing that makes *The Shocking Truth About Energy* special is that Loreen Leedy shares information from the point of view of an energy bolt named Erg. Why do you think she did that?

_____

_____

_____

_____

**2.** Why are sequence and transition words important in a book that explains a process, such as how coal, oil, water, and sunlight can be used to create electricity?

_____

_____

_____

_____

**3.** Loreen Leedy has also written and illustrated *My Teacher Is a Dinosaur, The Great Graph Contest, Mapping Penny's World, Fraction Action*, and *The Great Trash Bash*. Each of these books combines colorful characters and science or math facts. What topic do you think Leedy should tackle next? Why?

_____

_____

_____

_____

# Write-On Sheet

# [ Focus on Grammar and Usage ]

Write two sentences that contain correct use of prepositions.

1. _____

_____

_____

2. _____

_____

_____

> 66 Words set things in motion. I've seen them doing it. Words set up atmospheres, electrical fields, charges. 99
>
> —Toni Cade Bambara

# [ "Linking Words" Chart ]

Loreen Leedy presents reasons we should use fewer fossil fuels. In the chart below, under the appropriate header, write the sequence words and transition words she uses to move from one persuasive statement to the next.

Use linking words IF you want SO you can make your point AND be heard BUT don't overdo it. Like me.

### Loreen Leedy's Linking Words

| Compare or Contrast | Time Sequence | Added Information | Summary |
|---|---|---|---|
|  |  |  |  |
|  |  |  |  |
|  |  |  |  |

Write down two sentences that show Leedy's good use of sequence words and transition words.

1. _____

   _____

   _____

2. _____

   _____

   _____

- Establishing a Tone
- **Conveying the Purpose** ·····················
- Creating a Connection to the Audience
- Taking Risks to Create Voice

**Focus Mode: Persuasive**

# Voice

**"Voice is how you speak to readers. It's how you connect to them and show how much you care about your main idea, whether you're writing fiction or nonfiction. It's the energy in your writing."**

# Conveying the Purpose

The voice you use in a piece of writing should match your purpose for writing the piece. If you're writing a letter of thanks, your tone might be appreciative or grateful. But if you're writing a letter of complaint, your tone might be frustrated or upset. Use your voice to convey what you think and how you feel. Don't leave any doubt in your reader's mind.

How do you think the tone of Martin Luther King, Jr.'s speech helped convey his purpose?

# Reasons for Writing

Read the different writing formats in the chart below. Write the purpose, or reason, for writing each one (to persuade, to explain, or to tell a story). Then write the tone of voice you would use for each one (e.g., serious, friendly, knowledgeable, entertaining, convincing, excited, frustrated).

| **Thank-You Note** | **Help Wanted Ad** | **Party Invitation** |
|---|---|---|
| Purpose: _____ _____ Tone: _____ | Purpose: _____ _____ Tone: _____ | Purpose: _____ _____ Tone: _____ |
| **Instructions** | **Job Application** | **Postcard** |
| Purpose: _____ _____ Tone: _____ | Purpose: _____ _____ Tone: _____ | Purpose: _____ _____ Tone: _____ |

# Warm-Up 8

The little pig's house is not very sturdy, nor is this paragraph. Let your voice come breaking through!

**Is the writer's purpose for writing this paragraph clear?**

A house made of straw is not very sturdy. Let me tell you about when I used to live next door to the Three Little Pigs. I didn't try to eat the Three Little Pigs. I'm innocent.

**Revise the paragraph here or on a separate sheet.**

## Think About

- Is the purpose of my writing clear?
- Does my point of view come through?
- Is this the right tone for this kind of writing?
- Have I used strong voice throughout this piece?

Preview

# A Product Developer

**In the spaces below, write your thoughts and questions about the job of a product developer.**

1. A product developer must have a good time finding ways to make items appealing to people. This is what I think a product developer does:

   _____

   _____

   _____

2. Where I think I've seen a product developer's work:

   _____

   _____

   _____

3. Questions I have about how a product developer gets the job done:

   _____

   _____

   _____

   _____

4. What's the most appealing packaging you've ever seen? What makes it work for you?

   _____

   _____

   _____

   _____

# Write-On Sheet

**Voice:** Conveying the Purpose

## [ My Spelling Words ]

List your nine spelling words for the week here.

1.

2.

3.

4.

5.

6.

7.

8.

9.

> **"**The idea is to write it so that people hear it and it slides right through the brain and goes straight to the heart.**"**
>
> —Maya Angelou

# [ Persuasive Packaging ]

Look at a variety of labeled products and choose one to repackage. Create a more persuasive label.

**Product Name:**

_____

**Unique Product Features:**

_____

_____

_____

**Why this product is better than any others like it:**

_____

_____

_____

_____

_____

_____

_____

**New Slogan:**

_____

_____

_____

_____

Write your label on a separate sheet of paper and design it, using art supplies.

This product is quacktastic! I'm all feathered up!

Voice

- Applying Strong Verbs
- **Selecting Striking Words and Phrases** ················
- Using Specific and Accurate Words
- Choosing Words That Deepen Meaning

**Focus Mode: Persuasive**

# Word Choice

**❝Using the right words allows you to show what is happening in your piece or what matters to you about your topic. Precise and accurate words help make your main idea stand out.❞**

# Selecting Striking Words and Phrases

Striking words and phrases make your writing sparkle. Readers feel like they're inside your piece, rather than on the sidelines. Precise, descriptive words and phrases linger in the mind. Readers think about the piece long after they have finished reading it. They think bling, not blah!

**How is a treasure chest of eye-catching jewelry and coins similar to writing that contains striking words and phrases?**

# Word Wise

Imagery and figurative language can make your writing shine.

**Imagery** is language that focuses on the senses (sight, hearing, smell, touch, taste).

**Figurative language** uses expressions to describe, compare, or clarify points in creative ways.

| **Simile** | **Metaphor** |
|---|---|
| compares two unlike things using *like* or *as* | compares two unlike things without using *like* or *as* |
| *She runs like the wind.* *He's as strong as an ox.* | *You are my sunshine.* *Life is a roller coaster.* |
| **Hyperbole** | **Alliteration** |
| an exaggeration for emphasis | repetition of a starting sound |
| *Your book weighs a ton!* *I could eat a million of these!* | *Sample our sizzling steak smothered in savory sauce.* |

### Types of Figurative Language

**Read each sentence. Which type of literary technique did the writer use?**

1. I'm so tired I could sleep for a year! _____

2. This bland muffin is as hard as a rock. _____

3. Rouse your readers with remarkable writing. _____

4. The dainty daffodil fluttered and danced playfully in the breeze. _____

5. You can feel the clouds of comfort when you sit on this cozy couch. _____

# Warm-Up 9

Think "outside the box" and surprise your readers with some cool words and phrases!

**How striking are the words and phrases in this paragraph?**

Would you like to see what's inside this box? It's a surprise. It might be good. But, it might be bad. So buy this box now and find out its secret. It only costs a few dollars.

**Revise the paragraph here or on a separate sheet.**

## Think About

- Did I try to use words that sound *just right*?
- Did I try hyphenating several shorter words to make an interesting-sounding new word?
- Did I try putting together words with the same sound?
- Did I read my piece aloud to find at least one or two moments I love?

# Word Choice: **Selecting Striking Words and Phrases**

# David Stewart, author of
## *You Wouldn't Want to Be an Egyptian Mummy!*
**Read the information about David Stewart and answer two of the questions below.**

David Stewart lives in Brighton, England, but his books are read all over the world. He's written nonfiction on many subjects, from tadpoles to the *Titanic*. His most popular books are part of a fun, fact-filled series called You Wouldn't Want to.... These books invite readers to imagine what it would be like to live through some of the most ghastly episodes of the past. Titles include *You Wouldn't Want to Be Tutankhamen!*, *You Wouldn't Want to Sail on the Titanic!*, and *You Wouldn't Want to Be a Roman Soldier!* Stewart's words and David Antram's cartoon-style pictures make learning history fun. Even the back covers are filled with surprising facts!

1. What do you think you will learn about ancient Egypt from David Stewart's *You Wouldn't Want to Be an Egyptian Mummy!*?

_____

_____

_____

2. Which of David Stewart's other books would you most like to read? Why?

_____

_____

_____

3. Sometimes, the back cover of a book persuades people to open the book and read it. What striking words and phrases do you expect to find on the back cover of *You Wouldn't Want to Be an Egyptian Mummy!*?

_____

_____

# Write-On Sheet

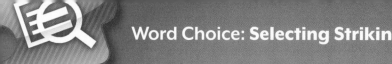

# [ Focus on Grammar and Usage ]

Write two sentences that contain correct use of subject-verb agreement.

1. _____

_____

_____

2. _____

_____

_____

> 66 Don't tell me the moon is shining; show me the glint of light on broken glass. 99
>
> —Anton Chekhov

# [ *You Wouldn't Want to Be an Egyptian Mummy!* Graphic Organizer ]

Read the ordinary words and phrases below. In the blank boxes, write the striking words and phrases Stewart used on the back cover to say the same things.

Mummy mia! Unwrap some great mummy words.

**Ordinary Words and Phrases**

**Striking Words and Phrases David Stewart Used**

| | |
|---|---|
| You are a rich Egyptian and about to die.  | |
| Your body goes through a long series of steps to become a mummy.  | |
| It's not great!  | |
| Put some rags in the body to make it look real.  | |

# [Persuasive Publishing Checklist]

Think you are ready to go public with your extended persuasive project? Use this form to make sure you've covered all the writing bases.

Be persuasive!
Be convincing!
Be oh-so-cooool!

**I remembered to**

☐ state my position on the topic clearly and stick with it while also exposing weaknesses in other positions.

☐ offer good, sound reasoning based on solid facts, opinions, and examples that originate from reliable, objective sources.

☐ develop my argument logically, using solid reasoning from beginning to end.

☐ use a compelling, confident voice to add credibility.

☐ explain any unusual words, phrases, or concepts.

☐ read my piece aloud to check how it will sound to the reader.

☐ proofread my piece carefully and clean up problems with conventions.

The purpose of my piece is

_____

The most critical point I make is

_____

What I hope readers will take away from my piece is

_____

Presentation

**Focus Mode: Expository**

Whether your topic is elephants, Estonia, or volcanic eruptions, the main purpose of expository writing is to inform or explain. That said, your piece does not need to be a list of facts. In reality, it shouldn't be. Think about including fascinating details, intriguing insights, and life experiences. Good expository writing is written in a strong, confident voice—a voice that tells the reader you know what you're talking about.

- Crafting Well-Built Sentences
- **Varying Sentence Types** ··········
- Capturing Smooth and Rhythmic Flow
- Breaking the "Rules" to Create Fluency

**Focus Mode: Expository**

# Sentence Fluency

Sentence Fluency

**"To create sentence fluency, you have to read with your ears *and* eyes. Make your writing sound as good as it looks by building sentences that flow smoothly from one to the next."**

# Varying Sentence Types

Do you want to know the secret to making your writing sound great? Include sentences of all kinds—short ones, long ones, and medium-sized ones. Include statements, questions, commands, and exclamations. Mix it up! Varying sentence types gives your ideas color and texture.

**How is using a variety of sentence types like weaving a colorful cloth?**

# Viva Variety!

**Use a variety of sentence structures in your writing to make it flow.**

## Types of Sentence Structures

▶ **Simple:** a sentence made up of one independent clause that may contain a direct object or prepositional phrase

"<u>The students chose</u> <u>a book</u>."
    independent clause    direct object

"<u>The students raved</u> <u>about the book</u>."
    independent clause    prepositional phrase

▶ **Compound:** a sentence made up of two or more independent clauses that are joined by a conjunction such as *and, but,* or *or*

"<u>The students raved about the book,</u> <u>and</u>
    independent clause        conjunction

<u>the author enjoyed receiving their fan mail</u>."
    independent clause

▶ **Complex:** a sentence made up of an independent clause and at least one dependent clause

"<u>When the author learned how much the students liked her work,</u>
    dependent clause

<u>she decided to write more books</u>."
    independent clause

**Combine the sentences in these paragraphs to create more variety.**

1. Some trains are powered by steam. Some trains are powered by diesel fuel. Some trains are powered by electricity.

_____

_____

2. France has a train powered by electricity. It's a high-speed train. Japan has a high-speed train. It's powered by magnetic force. Do you know the source of that magnetic force?

_____

_____

# Warm-Up 10

Hop on track with fluency.

**How is this paragraph's sentence variety?**

An orphan is a kid with no parents. The Orphan Train Movement started in 1854. The Orphan Train Movement ended in 1929. More than 100,000 children were part of it. Most came from New York City or Boston. They were sent to farms in the West. Myrtle and Cliff Jennings rode on an Orphan Train in 1912. Myrtle and Cliff traveled from New York to Wheeler, Arkansas.

**Revise the paragraph here or on a separate sheet.**

## Think About

- Did I include different kinds of sentences?
- Are some of my sentences complex?
- Are some of my sentences simple?
- Did I intermingle types of sentence structures?

**Preview**

# Christine King Farris, author of

## *My Brother Martin*

**Read the information about Christine King Farris below, and then answer the questions.**

Christine King Farris is the older sister of Martin Luther King, Jr. She wrote *My Brother Martin,* a picture book for children, to tell about her childhood with her brother. In the book, she shares her favorite childhood memories, such as when her brother played pranks on family and friends. Her goal in writing the book was to show a more personal side to Martin, since most people only know him as a civil rights leader. Christine King Farris now teaches at Spelman College in Atlanta, Georgia. Since her mother was a teacher, she wanted to be one too. Working with students brings Christine King Farris much joy because they motivate her with their smiles and eagerness to learn.

1. List two facts about Christine King Farris that you find interesting.

   _____

   _____

   _____

2. How does Christine King Farris use her life experiences in her writing?

   _____

   _____

   _____

3. What do you think you will learn about Martin Luther King, Jr., from reading Christine King Farris's book *My Brother Martin*?

   _____

   _____

   _____

# Write-On Sheet

# [ My Spelling Words ]

List your nine spelling words for the week here.

1.

2.

3.

4.

5.

6.

7.

8.

9.

> 66 I learned to write by listening to people talk. I still feel that the best of my writing comes from having heard rather than having read. 99
>
> —Gayl Jones

# [ *My Brother Martin Sentence Chart* ]

In *My Brother Martin,* Christine King Farris shares memories about growing up with her younger brother, Martin Luther King, Jr. What are your favorite parts of the book? Summarize them by writing your own short (simple) and long (compound, complex) sentences.

| short sentence | |
|---|---|
| long sentence | |

| short sentence | |
|---|---|
| long sentence | |

| short sentence | |
|---|---|
| long sentence | |

- Finding a Topic
- Focusing the Topic
- **Developing the Topic** ....................
- Using Details

**Focus Mode: Expository**

# Ideas

**"Write about things you care about, wonder about, and notice. Then use lots of juicy, sensory details to describe those things. Great ideas make all the difference in writing!"**

Ideas

# Developing the Topic

When you develop your topic, you flesh out your main idea. You think deeply about why you're writing the piece and what your reader needs to know in order to understand it. You stretch to express yourself. As a result, your writing bursts with color and stands strong.

**How is a blossoming bud like a developing piece of writing?**

# Fact Finder

Time to put on your detective cap and investigate. Gather facts to develop your topic into a fabulous piece of writing.

## How to Gather Facts

1. **Brainstorm** what you know and what you want to find out.

2. **Research** to find fascinating facts and answers to questions.

3. **Sort and group** your facts. Remove information you don't need or want.

## What to Collect

| WHO | WHERE | WHEN |
|---|---|---|
| participants | setting | time period |
| • Think about characters, important people, cultures, and backgrounds. | • Think about locations, origins, and destinations. | • Think about the past, present, and future. |

| WHY | WHAT | HOW |
|---|---|---|
| reasons for something happening, or for someone's actions | main events, items, and issues | plan or process |
| • Think about the purpose of the event or motivation for acting. | • Think about goals and results. | • Think about sequence, strategy, and actions. |

**Gather facts about your topic—important, intriguing, extraordinary ones!**

# Warm-Up 11

Watermelons are swell, but bananas are much easier to carry.

**Is this paragraph's topic developed?**

There are many different types of melons. Watermelons are the most popular. They are hard on the outside and soft and sweet on the inside.

**Revise the paragraph here or on a separate sheet.**

## Think About

- Am I sure my information is right?
- Are my details chock-full of interesting information?
- Have I used details that show new thinking about this idea?
- Will my reader believe what I say about this topic?

**Preview**

# A Toy Company Writer

**In the spaces below, fill in your thoughts about what a toy company writer does. What questions do you have about the job?**

1. What I think a toy company writer does:

   _____

   _____

   _____

   _____

   _____

2. Give some examples of where you think you've seen a toy company writer's work:

   _____

   _____

   _____

   _____

   _____

3. Questions I have about the job:

   _____

   _____

   _____

   _____

   _____

# Write-On Sheet

# [ Focus on Grammar and Usage ]

Write two sentences—one about something that happened in the past and one about something that will happen in the future. Be sure to use the correct verb tense in each sentence.

1. _____

   _____

2. _____

   _____

" I love revision. Where else in life can spilled milk be transformed into ice cream? "

—Katherine Paterson

# [ Toy Development Team ]

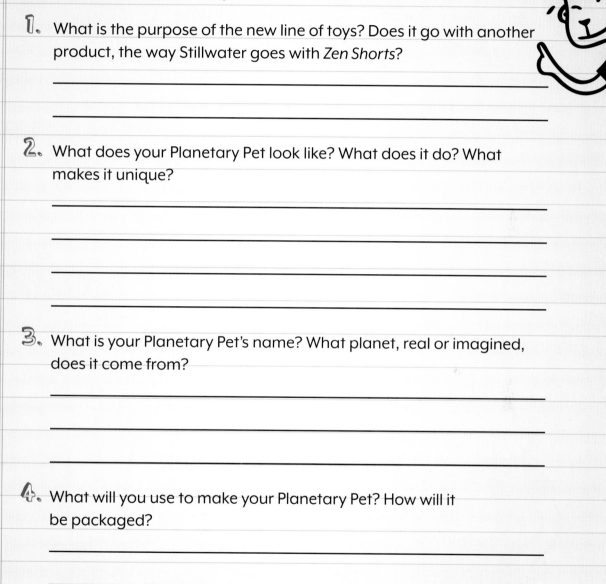

**Outer space? No, thanks, I get dizzy!**

**Help develop a new line of dolls called Planetary Pets, creatures from outer space. Answer the questions below about a creature of your own creation.**

1. What is the purpose of the new line of toys? Does it go with another product, the way Stillwater goes with *Zen Shorts*?

   _____

   _____

2. What does your Planetary Pet look like? What does it do? What makes it unique?

   _____

   _____

   _____

   _____

3. What is your Planetary Pet's name? What planet, real or imagined, does it come from?

   _____

   _____

   _____

4. What will you use to make your Planetary Pet? How will it be packaged?

   _____

   _____

   _____

   _____

**Use your answers to write a product description about your Planetary Pal on a separate sheet of paper. Include a picture.**

- Creating the Lead
- Using Sequence Words and Transition Words
- **Structuring the Body** ·······························
- Ending With a Sense of Resolution

**Focus Mode: Expository**

# Organization

**"Organization is about the structure of a piece of writing. Nothing holds your piece together—or holds a reader's attention—better than sturdy, easy-to-follow organization."**

# Structuring the Body

When you apply this key quality well, you create a piece that is tight. You present details logically and use them to support your big idea. You slow down and speed up at just the right points. As a result, your message sticks in the mind of your reader.

How is structuring the body of a piece of writing like creating a spider web?

# Nonfiction Text Structures

The body of a piece of nonfiction can be organized in lots of different ways. Here are five structures writers often use.

**1.** **Description or List:** a set or group of items
**Homework**

1. Read Chapter 3 in art history book.

2. Finish math.

3. Revise paragraphs 4 and 5 of autobiography and work on details.

4. Read newspaper article on my favorite pop star.

**2.** **Sequence or Time Order:** a series of events or steps in a process
*First,* consult homework list.   *Then,* gather books and papers.
*Finally,* begin the assignments.

**3.** **Compare and Contrast:** similarities and differences between two people, places, or things

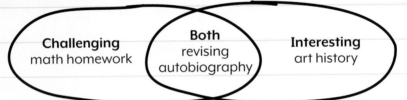

**Challenging**
math homework

**Both**
revising
autobiography

**Interesting**
art history

**4.** **Cause and Effect:** an action or idea and how it came to be

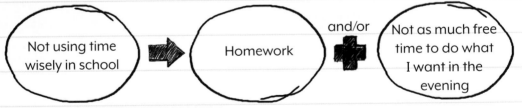

Not using time wisely in school

Homework

and/or

Not as much free time to do what I want in the evening

**5.** **Problem and Solution:** a dilemma of some sort and possible ways out of it

I left the pop-star article at school.

Call a friend and borrow hers

Download it from a website

# Warm-Up 12

order put paragraph this Please in! (Oops.)

**How is this paragraph's structure?**

A butterfly is hatched. From the eggs hatch larvae, or caterpillars. The egg is laid. The caterpillar turns into a chrysalis and hibernates.

**Revise the paragraph here or on a separate sheet.**

## Think About

- Have I shown the reader where to slow down and where to speed up?
- Do all the details fit where they are placed?
- Will the reader find it easy to follow my ideas?
- Does the organization help the main idea stand out?

## Organization: **Structuring the Body**

**Preview**

# Nic Bishop, author of *Spiders*

Find a partner and answer two of the questions below.

1. Read the titles of some of Nic Bishop's books below. What kinds of books does he write?

| | |
|---|---|
| *Lizards* | *Backyard Detective* |
| *Marsupials* | *Quest for the Tree Kangaroo* |

_____

_____

_____

_____

2. Which of Nic Bishop's books would you most like to read? Why?

_____

_____

_____

_____

_____

3. Nic Bishop both writes his books and takes the photographs for them. How do you think his photos affect what he writes?

_____

_____

_____

_____

_____

_____

# Write-On Sheet

# [ My Spelling Words ]

List your nine spelling words for the week here.

1.
2.
3.
4.
5.
6.
7.
8.
9.

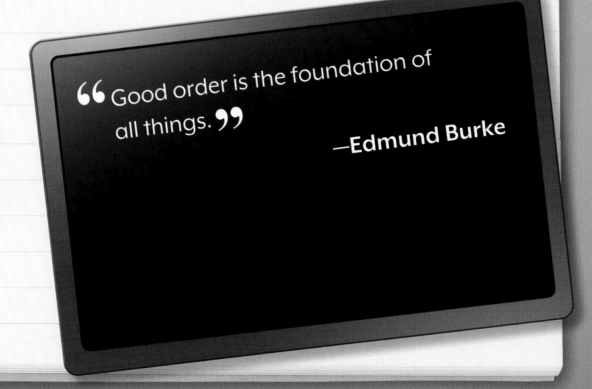

66 Good order is the foundation of all things. 99

—Edmund Burke

# [ *Spiders Graphic Organizer* ]

Spiders are so cool—and Nic Bishop's book is crawling with them. List three characteristics and three behaviors that you think are the coolest.

On a separate sheet of paper, use your cool facts to write a short, well-structured piece about spiders.

# [ Expository Publishing Checklist ]

**Think you are ready to go public with your expository unit project? Use this form to make sure you've covered all the writing bases.**

As we say where I live, you've got this piece down COLD!

**I remembered to**

☐ include facts that came from reliable sources.

☐ weave in details that show how much I know about my topic.

☐ develop the topic logically from beginning to end.

☐ use a voice that expresses my fascination for the topic.

☐ explain any unusual words, phrases, or concepts.

☐ read my piece aloud to check how it will sound to the readers.

☐ proofread my piece carefully and clean up problems with conventions.

The purpose of my piece is

_____

_____

The part that works best is

_____

_____

What I hope readers will take away from my piece is

_____

_____

_____

Presentation

### Focus Mode: Narrative

Whether you're writing about a visit from space aliens or a day at an amusement park, the main purpose of narrative writing is to tell a story. Your narrative pieces should include characters, a setting, events, a problem to be solved—and maybe a surprise or two. They should capture your reader's interest and hang on to it, right to the end.

- Establishing a Tone
- Conveying the Purpose
- **Creating a Connection to the Audience** ···························
- Taking Risks to Create Voice

**Focus Mode: Narrative**

# Voice

Voice

**"Voice is how you speak to readers. It's how you connect to them and show how much you care about your main idea, whether you're writing fiction or nonfiction. It's the energy in your writing."**

# Creating a Connection to the Audience

If you're having trouble choosing the right voice, think about who is going to read the piece when it's finished. Who is your audience? Use your voice to connect with readers so they want to listen to what you have to say. Tell them what you think and feel. Make them understand what matters to you!

How do singers and writers connect to their audience?

# My Mistake

Everyone makes mistakes, right? Follow these steps to write
a letter about a big mistake you made.

1. **Choose a target audience, such as**

| | | |
|---|---|---|
| my best friend | kids my age | someone I hurt |
| a young child | an older relative | a family member |

My audience will be _____.

2. **Choose the right tone of voice for that audience, such as**

| | | |
|---|---|---|
| humorous | apologetic | honest |
| friendly | mysterious | worried |

My voice will be _____.

3. **Choose a purpose for writing the letter, such as to say**

| | | |
|---|---|---|
| This was amazing. | I learned a lesson. | I'm truly sorry. |
| I'll never give up. | I'm not afraid to try. | We should do it again! |

Now write the lead sentence(s) in a letter about your big mistake.
Match your tone of voice to your target audience. Express how you feel.

Dear _____,

_____

_____

_____

_____

_____

_____

_____

# Warm-Up 13

"Bow wow wow." Is that voice or just dog-gone dull?

**How is this paragraph's connection to the audience?**

The golden retriever is my favorite kind of dog. They are nice and loyal dogs. I had one when I was younger.

**Revise the paragraph here or on a separate sheet.**

## Think About

- Have I thought about the reader?
- Is this the right voice for this audience?
- Have I shown what matters most to me in this piece?
- Will the reader know how I think and feel about the topic?

**Preview**

# A Comic Book Author

In the spaces below, write down what you know a comic book author does. What questions do you have about the job?

**1.** What makes a comic book different from other books?
What would a comic book author find challenging about his or her work?

_____

_____

_____

_____

_____

**2.** Some examples of comic books I've read or comic book characters I know:

_____

_____

_____

_____

_____

**3.** Questions I'd like to ask a comic book author:

_____

_____

_____

_____

_____

# Write-On Sheet

# [ Focus on Grammar and Usage ]

Write two sets of sentences—one set about something that happened in the past and one set about something that happens in the present. Be sure verb tenses agree in each set of sentences.

1. _____

   _____

   _____

   _____

2. _____

   _____

   _____

   _____

> 66 Listen to yourself. If you are excited by what you are writing, you have a much better chance of putting that excitement over to a reader. 99
>
> —Robin McKinley

# [ "Ultraviolet" Web ]

Use the web to record the target audience for "Ultraviolet" and the ways Jake Bell connects to that audience.

Target Audience for "Ultraviolet":

_____

Ouch! Use the web, not my webbed feet!

Ways the Writer Connects to the Audience

- Applying Strong Verbs
- Selecting Striking Words and Phrases
- **Using Specific and Accurate Words** ...............................
- Choosing Words That Deepen Meaning

**Focus Mode: Narrative**

# Word Choice

**"Using the right words allows you to show what is happening in your piece or what matters to you about your topic. Precise and accurate words help make your main idea stand out."**

# Using Specific and Accurate Words

Imagine if writers had only "blue" to describe the range of hues for that color. We'd miss specific and accurate writing like: "the blue of my grandmother's Navajo turquoise bracelet," or "my parakeet's sapphire and aqua feathers." Writers know the importance of "just right" words and phrases, just as you might look for the "just right" shade for the walls of your room.

**How is choosing just the right paint color for a room like choosing just the right word for a piece of writing?**

## Specific and Accurate Clues

**Part 1:** Draw a T-shirt design in the box below. Write three specific and accurate clues to describe your design. Don't show your work to anyone.

My T-Shirt Design

**My Clues**

1. _____

   _____

   _____

2. _____

   _____

   _____

3. _____

   _____

**Part 2:** Turn back-to-back with a partner. Tell your partner your clues. Have him or her draw your T-shirt design. Switch roles and compare drawings.

My Partner's T-Shirt Design

# Warm-Up 14

Does this paragraph contain specific and accurate words?

> My best friend is so nice. She's funny. She's really funny when we go to the mall and hang out together. We like to do fun things that make us laugh a lot. When we go out to eat we always order good things.

Revise the paragraph here or on a separate sheet.

Next time they're at the mall, they should check out the Word Shop!

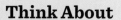

**Think About**

- Have I used nouns and modifiers that help the reader see a picture?
- Did I avoid using words that might confuse the reader?
- Did I try a new word and, if so, check to make sure I've used it correctly?
- Are these the best words I can use?

**Preview**

# Jan Romero Stevens, author of

*Carlos and the Squash Plant*

**Find a partner and answer two of the questions below.**

1. Read the titles of some of Jan Romero Stevens's books below. What kinds of books does she write? Which book would you like to read most? Why?

   *Carlos and the Skunk*           *Carlos Digs to China*

   *Carlos and the Carnival*        *Carlos and the Cornfield*

   _____

   _____

   _____

   _____

2. Stevens created a popular character named Carlos, who appears in all the books listed above. What makes a great series character?

   _____

   _____

   _____

   _____

3. Stevens lived in the Southwest her whole life. The culture, history, food, and people of that region inspired her as a writer. Is there something about where you live that inspires you as a writer?

   _____

   _____

   _____

# Write-On Sheet

# [ My Spelling Words ]

List your nine spelling words for the week here.

1.

2.

3.

4.

5.

6.

7.

8.

9.

> ❝The idea is to get the pencil moving quickly. . . . Once you've got some words looking back at you, you can take two or three, throw them away, and look for others.❞
>
> —Bernard Malamud

# [ Carlos and the Squash Plant Charts ]

In *Carlos and the Squash Plant,* Jan Romero Stevens chose many precise words to paint vivid pictures in her readers' minds. Complete the charts by filling in words from the book.

I dropped a squash once. Yes, I squished a squash.

Word Choice

| Foods Grown and Eaten by the Family | |
|---|---|
| Specific Words | Accurate Words |
| | |

| Carlos's Squash Plant | |
|---|---|
| Specific Words | Accurate Words |
| | |

- Crafting Well-Built Sentences
- Varying Sentence Types
- **Capturing Smooth and Rhythmic Flow** ••••••••••••••••••••
- Breaking the "Rules" to Create Fluency

**Focus Mode: Narrative**

# Sentence Fluency

Sentence Fluency

**❝To create sentence fluency, you have to read with your ears *and* eyes. Make your writing sound as good as it looks by building sentences that flow smoothly from one to the next.❞**

# Capturing Smooth and Rhythmic Flow

When you capture smooth and rhythmic flow in your writing, you transform tired, awkward sentences into fresh, natural-sounding ones. You bring a musical quality to your piece by varying sentence lengths and beginnings, picking just-right words, and using transitions to keep your message moving along and sounding sweet.

**How is experiencing a great piece of writing like experiencing a great piece of music?**

# Techniques for Creating Flow

**Technique 1: Using Sequence and Transition Words**

Sequence and transition words link ideas within and between sentences.
Use them to bring flow to your writing.

| Where | | When | | To compare | |
|---|---|---|---|---|---|
| above | in back of | first | meanwhile | like | however |
| between | to the left | while | as soon as | similarly | instead |
| near | in the distance | lately | tomorrow | but | or |
| How or Why | | To extend | | To close | |
| naturally | for this reason | another | besides | consequently | all in all |
| truly | to be specific | furthermore | again | in summary | finally |
| actually | to repeat | for example | in addition | in conclusion | therefore |

**Technique 2: Varying Sentence Lengths and Types**

Combining sentences helps vary sentence lengths and improves flow. Using a variety of sentence types—simple, compound, complex—does that, too.

**Technique 3: Varying Sentence Beginnings**

If all your sentences begin in the same way, your writing will sound choppy. Changing some of the beginnings will improve the flow.

**Original Paragraph:**

I was in a rowboat on the lake. I saw some black clouds. I knew I had to get back in. I grabbed for the oars. I lost one.

**Revision Using Techniques 1, 2, and 3:**

I was in the rowboat on the lake when suddenly I noticed some black clouds in the distance. A storm was coming! Quickly, I grabbed for the oars, but dropped one in the water. What was I to do?

# Warm-Up 15

I've got flow. You've got flow. This paragraph? No go on flow.

**How well does this paragraph flow?**

Doing chores is boring. I hate taking out the trash. I hate cleaning my room. I hate doing the dishes. I wish I didn't have to do chores.

**Revise the paragraph here or on a separate sheet.**

## Think About

- Is it easy to read the entire piece aloud?
- Do my sentences flow, one to the next?
- Do individual passages sound smooth when I read them aloud?
- Did I thoughtfully place different sentence types to enhance the main idea?

**Preview**

# Allan Sherman,

**author of** *Hello Muddah, Hello Faddah!*

**Find a partner and answer two of the questions below.**

1. *Hello Muddah, Hello Faddah!* was originally published as a song. What other songs do you know that have been turned into books?

_____

_____

_____

_____

_____

2. What other songs, in your opinion, should be turned into books? Why?

_____

_____

_____

_____

_____

3. *Hello Muddah, Hello Faddah!* is a letter from a kid at summer camp to his parents. What kinds of details can you find out about a person from a letter?

_____

_____

_____

_____

_____

# Write-On Sheet

# [ Focus on Grammar and Usage ]

Write two sentences that contain correct use of compound subjects and predicates.

1. _____

_____

_____

_____

2. _____

_____

_____

_____

> 66 In a conversation you can use timing, a look, an inflection. But on the page all you have are commas, dashes, and ... syllables in a word. When I write, I read everything out loud to get the right rhythm. 99
>
> —Fran Lebowitz

# [ What Makes a Song Sing? ]

*Hello Muddah, Hello Faddah!* was originally published as a song. Listen for and write down rhyming words that help create flow.

### Rhyming Words

- _____ and _____
- _____ and _____
- _____ and _____
- _____ and _____

- _____ and _____
- _____ and _____
- _____ and _____
- _____ and _____

Count the number of syllables in each line of the first stanza and write them down in the first chart.
Then do the same for the second stanza.
What do you notice about the syllable pattern?

### First Stanza

Line 1: _____ syllables

Line 2: _____ syllables

Line 3: _____ syllables

Line 4: _____ syllables

### Second Stanza

Line 1: _____ syllables

Line 2: _____ syllables

Line 3: _____ syllables

Line 4: _____ syllables

Hello readah, hello writah...

**Syllable Pattern:** _____ , _____ , _____ , _____

# [ Narrative Publishing Checklist ]

**Are you ready to go public with your extended narrative project? Use this form to make sure you've covered all the writing bases.**

Characters? Check.
Plot? Check.
Awesomeness? Check.

**I remembered to**

☐ develop a fascinating story line with interesting characters.

☐ include time and place that work well with the plotline.

☐ tell the story chronologically.

☐ use an active voice to entertain, surprise, and challenge the reader.

☐ choose words that enhance the characters, time, and place.

☐ read my piece aloud to check how it will sound to readers.

☐ proofread my piece carefully and clean up problems with conventions.

Conventions

The purpose of my piece is

_____

My favorite part is

_____

What I hope readers will find most memorable about my piece is

_____

_____

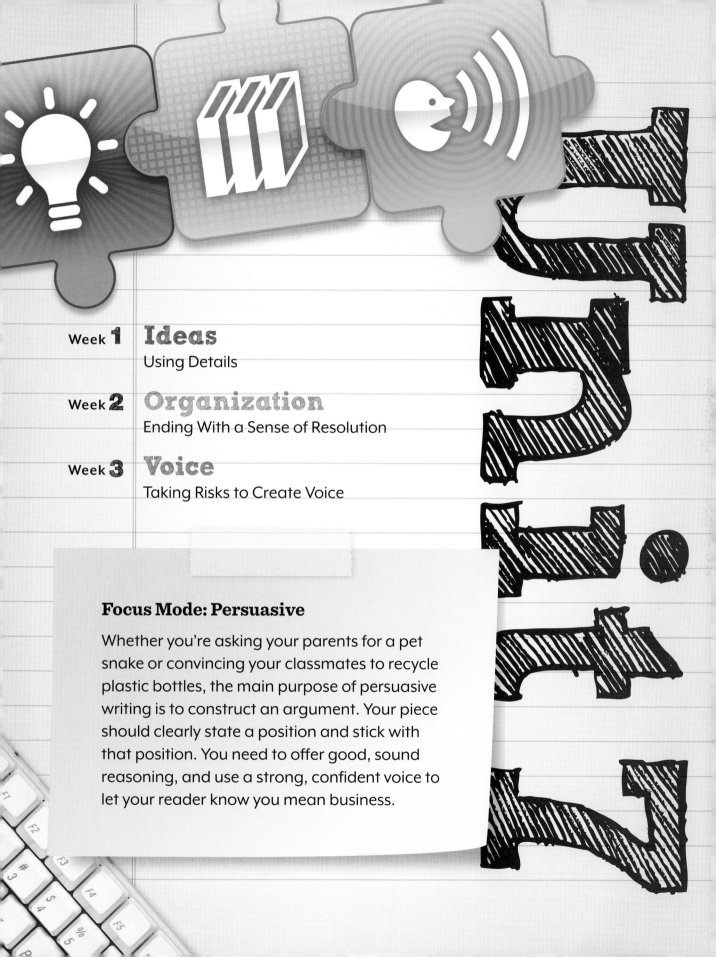

### Focus Mode: Persuasive

Whether you're asking your parents for a pet snake or convincing your classmates to recycle plastic bottles, the main purpose of persuasive writing is to construct an argument. Your piece should clearly state a position and stick with that position. You need to offer good, sound reasoning, and use a strong, confident voice to let your reader know you mean business.

- Finding a Topic
- Focusing the Topic
- Developing the Topic
- **Using Details** ·······································

**Focus Mode: Persuasive**

# Ideas

❝Write about things you care about, wonder about, and notice. Then use lots of juicy, sensory details to describe those things. Great ideas make all the difference in writing!❞

# Using Details

When you write, you want your readers to see exactly what you are thinking. Details help readers imagine how something looks, feels, smells, sounds, or tastes. They make your ideas clearer and easier to understand. Your piece becomes a feast for the senses.

**How is including details in writing like experiencing a rain storm with all your senses?**

## Listen to Your Senses

Take a short walk around your school. Use your senses to capture in the chart interesting, important, and unusual details you notice.

| | Tour Details |
|---|---|
| I saw . . . | |
| I heard . . . | |
| I smelled . . . | |
| I touched . . . | |
| I tasted . . . | |

Write a short letter to the principal explaining why you'd be a good school tour guide. Use details from the chart.

_____

_____

_____

_____

_____

_____

_____

# Warm-Up 16

C'mon! Blow me away with a deluge of disaster details.

**How are the details in this paragraph?**

Hurricane season happens once a year or so. Hurricanes do a lot of damage. Hurricanes have strong winds and can damage buildings and homes. You need to be prepared.

**Revise the paragraph here or on a separate sheet.**

## Think About

- Did I create a picture in the reader's mind?
- Did I use details that draw upon the five senses (sight, touch, taste, smell, hearing)?
- Do my details stay on the main topic?
- Did I stretch for details beyond the obvious?

## Ideas: **Using Details**

### Preview

# Mo Willems, author of

### *Don't Let the Pigeon Drive the Bus!*

### Find a partner and answer two of the questions below.

**1.** After he graduated from high school, Mo Willems decided to become a stand-up comic. He was not a success, but the experience helped him succeed at creating books because it taught him a lot about being funny. Think about a time you tried something and failed. What did you learn from the experience that might help you as a writer?

_____

_____

_____

_____

**2.** Mo Willems says his pigeon character became popular because it reminds many people, even Willems himself, of always being told "NO!" as a young child. Who is your favorite character from a book? Why?

_____

_____

_____

**3.** Pigeon is a popular character that appears in many of Mo Willems's books. What makes a great series character? Name some of your favorites.

_____

_____

_____

_____

# Write-On Sheet

# [ My Spelling Words ]

List your nine spelling words for the week here.

1.

2.

3.

4.

5.

6.

7.

8.

9.

❝The true secret of happiness lies in taking a genuine interest in all the details of daily life.❞

—William Morris

# [ How the Pigeon Persuades ]

The pigeon does his best to persuade you to let him drive the bus.
List four things the pigeon says and the method he uses to persuade
you—by asking, by begging, by negotiating, or by demanding.

| What the Pigeon Says | How the Pigeon Persuades |
|---|---|
| LET ME DRIVE THE BUS!!! | demanding |
| | |
| | |
| | |
| | |

Pigeons driving buses? What's next, monkeys with big ideas?

- Creating the Lead
- Using Sequence Words and Transition Words
- Structuring the Body
- **Ending With a Sense of Resolution** ............................

**Focus Mode: Persuasive**

# Organization

**❝Organization is about the structure of a piece of writing. Nothing holds your piece together—or holds a reader's attention—better than sturdy, easy-to-follow organization.❞**

# Ending With a Sense of Resolution

The conclusion is the final touch on a piece of writing—its last lines. A good conclusion ties up all the loose ends and makes your piece feel complete. It's your last word, so be sure to write something readers will remember.

**How is a dramatic sunset like the ending of a strong piece of writing?**

# Ending Strong

**Every piece of writing you create should have an ending that makes your readers feel satisfied. Try these techniques for creating strong endings.**

**Profound Thought**

The writer takes a little bit of information and elevates it to a higher level.

**Example:** *Adopting a pet from a shelter can save its life while adding joy to yours.*

**Quote**

The writer includes the words of others to reinforce key points.

**Example:** *Aesop said it best, "No act of kindness, no matter how small, is ever wasted."*

**Tie-Up**

The writer ties up loose ends and lingering questions.

**Example:** *To be clear, every cent we collect buys books for schools.*

**Open-Ended Question**

The writer gives the reader more to think about, using the information provided as a starting point.

**Example:** *Isn't that what you want from the president of your Student Council?*

**Challenge**

The writer urges the reader to take action.

**Example:** *Open your mind and listen. Your parents know more than you think.*

**Summary**

The writer rounds up key points that he or she made in the body of the piece.

**Example:** *Don't forget! Do your part for the planet by turning off the water when you brush your teeth, riding on a bus or in a train instead of a car, and recycling.*

**Laugh**

The writer makes the reader laugh by saying something humorous at the end.

**Example:** *I skidded and slipped, tripped and stumbled across the floor as my friends howled. Here's a tip: When a sign says, "Slippery When Wet," believe it!*

# Warm-Up 17

**I vote for a better ending. And no recounts allowed!**

**How is this paragraph's conclusion?**

And now you know the three reasons why kids should be allowed to vote. So in conclusion, I hope you learned something from my paper.

**Revise the paragraph here or on a separate sheet.**

## Think About

- Have I wrapped up all the loose ends?
- Have I ended at the best place?
- Do I have an ending that makes my writing feel finished?
- Did I leave the reader with something to think about?

**Preview**

# Lauren Thompson, author of

*Hope Is an Open Heart*

**Find a partner and answer two of the questions below.**

1. When she writes, Lauren Thompson often calls on memories of childhood experiences, small moments that felt special or important to her. What is a memory that you'd like to write about?

   _____

   _____

   _____

   _____

2. Lauren Thompson wrote *Hope Is an Open Heart* in part to support Save the Children, a not-for-profit organization that helps children all over the world by providing education and health care. In what other ways do you think a book can help someone?

   _____

   _____

   _____

   _____

3. Lauren Thompson's book *Hope Is an Open Heart* is all about different expressions of hope. How do you express hope? What makes you feel hopeful?

   _____

   _____

   _____

   _____

# Write-On Sheet

# [ Focus on Grammar and Usage ]

Write two sentences in which you correctly use adjectives that compare.

1. _____

_____

_____

2. _____

_____

_____

❝It is good to have an end to journey towards; but it is the journey that matters in the end.❞

—Ursula Le Guin

# [ Afterword Outline ]

Lauren Thompson concludes *Hope Is an Open Heart* with a persuasive afterword. Record her opinion statement about the importance of hope; facts, reasons, and examples she includes to persuade you to accept her opinion; and her final appeal.

**Opinion Statement**

_____

_____

↓

**Supporting Facts, Reasons, Examples**

- _____

- _____

- _____

- _____

↓

**Final Appeal**

_____

_____

Hope is an open bag of dog food.

Organization

- Establishing a Tone
- Conveying the Purpose
- Creating a Connection to the Audience
- **Taking Risks to Create Voice** . . . . . . . . . . . . . . . . . . .

**Focus Mode: Persuasive**

Voice

**" Voice is how you speak to readers. It's how you connect to them and show how much you care about your main idea, whether you're writing fiction or nonfiction. It's the energy in your writing. "**

# Taking Risks to Create Voice

The best writers take risks. They might write from a new perspective or experiment with unusual words. If you want your writing to be colorful, you can't be afraid to take chances and try new things. Surprise your readers. In the process, you might surprise yourself!

**Face paint makes you stand out from the crowd.
How can your writing do the same thing?**

# Taking Risks in Writing

**What risks are you willing to take to make your voice be heard? Consider these.**

1. Write from a perspective or point of view other than your own.

2. Reveal meaningful thoughts, experiences, or information.

3. Experiment with words or play with language.

**Read each paragraph below and identify which of the above techniques the writer used. Underline sentences that show evidence of that technique.**

1. A drought is no picnic, and I should know, I survived one. A drought is more than just brown lawns. A real drought, the kind I experienced, parches the land so thoroughly that it cracks like shattered glass. The corn on our farm, Mom's vegetable garden, and our two cows died because we didn't have enough water to keep them alive. I hated living through those terrible times. That's why saving the planet's water is so important to me—and it should be to you, too.

   **Technique:** _____

2. *Shrick. Shrack.* Did you hear that? That's the sound of my crust baking and cracking in the sun. A drought has pounded the life from me. My plants have dried up; and because their roots no longer hold it together, my soil has disintegrated into dust and blown away. Poof. Gone. Without plants and water, animals have died. And without plants and animals, people will die, too. Water is a life-giving resource. To save me—Earth— you must first save my water. Please keep it clean and plentiful for your sake and mine.

   **Technique:** _____

# Warm-Up 18

**Did the writer of this paragraph take any risks?**

Last night my coach finally put me in a game. I played my best game of basketball ever. It was very fun. I played the whole game. My team won. I should play in more games.

**Revise the paragraph here or on a separate sheet.**

BOR-ING! This writing is as flat as a pancake.

Voice

### Think About

- Have I used words that are not ordinary?
- Is my writing interesting, fresh, and original?
- Have I tried to make my writing sound like me?
- Have I tried something different from what I've done before?

**Preview**

# A Playwright

In the spaces below, fill in your thoughts about what a playwright does and how a playwright approaches his or her job.

1. What I think a playwright does:

_____

_____

_____

_____

_____

2. Some plays I've read or seen and what I thought about them:

_____

_____

_____

_____

_____

3. Questions I have about the job of a playwright:

_____

_____

_____

_____

_____

# Write-On Sheet

# [ My Spelling Words ]

List your nine spelling words for the week here.

1.
2.
3.
4.
5.
6.
7.
8.
9.

> **"** Don't say the old lady screamed—
> bring her on and let her scream. **"**
>
> —**Mark Twain**

# [ You're the Playwright ]

You've read Darien's monologue from *How to Eat Like a Child*, Lesson #21. Now it's your turn to write a scene for a play. In the box below, write the title, characters, and setting for your play. Then create a dialogue in which the characters try to persuade each other about something.

Scene 1: Good looking duck with a great voice enters stage left...

Title: _____

Characters: _____

Setting: _____

_____

_____

_____

_____

_____

_____

_____

_____

_____

_____

_____

_____

_____

# [ Persuasive Publishing Checklist ]

**Think you are ready to go public with your extended persuasive project? Use this form to make sure you've covered all the writing bases.**

Which is a better snack? Cheese or quackers?

**I remembered to**

☐ state my position on the topic clearly and stick with it, while also exposing weaknesses in other positions.

☐ offer good, sound reasoning based on solid facts, opinions, and examples that originate from reliable, objective sources.

☐ develop my argument logically, using solid reasoning from beginning to end.

☐ use a compelling, confident voice to add credibility.

☐ explain any unusual words, phrases, or concepts.

☐ read my piece aloud to check how it will sound to the reader.

☐ proofread my piece carefully and clean up problems with conventions.

The purpose of my piece is

_____

The most critical point I make is

_____

What I hope readers will take away from my piece is

_____

_____

### Focus Mode: Expository

Whether your topic is lizards, lacrosse, or Abraham Lincoln, the main purpose of expository writing is to inform or explain. That being said, your piece need not be a list of facts. Actually, it shouldn't be. Think about including fascinating details, intriguing insights, and life experiences. Good expository writing is written in a strong, confident voice—a voice that tells the reader you know what you're talking about.

- Applying Strong Verbs
- Selecting Striking Words and Phrases
- Using Specific and Accurate Words
- **Choosing Words That Deepen Meaning** ·······················

**Focus Mode: Expository**

# Word Choice

Word Choice

“**Using the right words allows you to show what is happening in your piece or what matters to you about your topic. Precise and accurate words help make your main idea stand out.**”

# Choosing Words That Deepen Meaning

Good writers take their time. They stop to think about the best words to use—words that make their message clear. So instead of using the first words that come to mind, dig deeper. Choose words that say exactly what you mean, paint pictures, and pack a punch. Give your readers something to think about.

**How is choosing words that deepen meaning like discovering a precious pearl inside an oyster?**

# Digging for Depth

Instead of skimming the surface, dig for the best words and phrases for your writing. Deepen the meaning of your message.

**Shallow:** I was scared.

**Slightly Deeper:** I was terrified.

**Really Deep:** My body shook with fear.

**As Deep as You Can Go:** Knees trembling, heart racing, sweat pouring . . . I was absolutely petrified!

How would you deepen the meaning of these sentences?

1. Pickles are good.

2. The fire was hot.

3. The girl was unhappy.

4. Cool painting!

5. Earthquakes move the earth.

Rewrite one sentence. Deepen its meaning. Go for gold!

**Shallow:**

**Slightly Deeper:**

**Really Deep:**

**As Deep as You Can Go:**

# Warm-Up 19

Lights in sight—words should be right!

**Do the words in this paragraph deepen its meaning?**

The Northern Lights are far away. Energy from the sun comes down to the poles and they light the sky up in different colors. They take different shapes, too.

**Revise the paragraph here or on a separate sheet.**

Word Choice

### Think About

- Did I think carefully about the words I chose?
- Have I tried to avoid repeating words?
- Will my words capture the reader's imagination?
- Have I found the best way to express myself?

**Preview**

# Avis Harley, author of *African Acrostics*

**Find a partner and answer two of the questions below.**

1. Read these titles of some of Avis Harley's books below. What kinds of books do you think she writes? Which of her books would you like to read most? Why?

   *African Acrostics*          *The Monarch's Progress: Poems With Wings*

   *Leap Into Poetry*          *Sea Stars: Saltwater Poems*

   _____

   _____

   _____

   _____

2. Think of a poem you like and write the title here. What do you like about the poem?

   _____

   _____

   _____

   _____

3. Avis Harley writes poems on topics such as animals and nature. Sometimes she includes factual notes about her topics at the back of her books. What topics do you hope she covers in the book *African Acrostics*?

   _____

   _____

   _____

   _____

# Write-On Sheet

# [ Focus on Conventions ]

Write two sentences that contain correct application of all conventions, including use of colons and the capitalization rules associated with that.

1. _____

_____

_____

2. _____

_____

_____

> 66 Don't use words too big for the subject. Don't say 'infinitely' when you mean 'very'; otherwise you'll have no word left when you want to talk about something really infinite. 99
>
> —C. S. Lewis

# [ Acrostic Animal Words ]

Cat words: elegant, finicky, dog-teasing...

Avis Harley uses rich, thought-provoking words to describe animals in *African Acrostics*. Choose three favorite poems from the book. Complete the chart for each one.

Animal: _____

Words the author used to deepen meaning:

Animal: _____

Words the author used to deepen meaning:

Animal: _____

Words the author used to deepen meaning:

- Crafting Well-Built Sentences
- Varying Sentence Types
- Capturing Smooth and Rhythmic Flow
- **Breaking the "Rules" to Create Fluency** ............................

**Focus Mode: Expository**

# Sentence Fluency

Sentence Fluency

**❝To create sentence fluency, you have to read with your ears *and* eyes. Make your writing sound as good as it looks by building sentences that flow smoothly from one to the next.❞**

# Breaking the "Rules" to Create Fluency

You have learned many rules for writing sentences correctly. "Always include a subject and verb." "Don't start a sentence with a conjunction." "Never use one word as a sentence." But wait! To bring rhythm to your writing, you might need to break the rules of conventions sometimes. Interjections can highlight points. And sentence fragments can add style. Shake it up. Break it up. Keep it flowing. Yes!

**How is breaking sentence writing rules like taking a detour as you drive down the road?**

# Fitting Fragments

Fragments are incomplete sentences that writers occasionally use to add impact, emphasize important ideas, and help their writing flow smoothly. Here are six creative ways to use fragments. Underline the fragment. Think about each fragment and how it could be turned into a complete sentence.

### ▶ Sound and Suspense

*He stood perfectly still. Ear to the door, listening. Waiting. Clip clop...clip clop.*

### ▶ Emotion and Exclamation

*Wow! What a spectacular view!*

### ▶ Emphasis of a Point

*Earthquakes rock the world. Really rock it. Feel the shake, rattle, and roll!*

### ▶ Answer to a Question

*Should we help planet Earth? Absolutely!*

### ▶ Dialogue

*"Hey Sue, wanna play some basketball after school?"*
*"Nah. Can't. Got too much homework."*

### ▶ Poetry

*Little star, shining bright.*
*Twinkling in the pale moonlight.*

**Choose one of the formats below. Write a fragment that might be used in that format.**

1. Song Lyrics
2. Spooky Story
3. Phone Conversation
4. Recipe
5. Sports Commentary

Format:

_____

Fragment:

_____

_____

_____

# Warm-Up 20

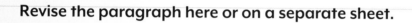

**Breaking rules will create just the right bounce!**

**Did this writer break the rules to create fluency?**

Some people say Ben Franklin proved that lightning is electricity. He and his son William flew a kite in a thunderstorm. The kite's string had a key on it. Electricity from the charged clouds traveled to the key, letting off a spark.

**Revise the paragraph here or on a separate sheet.**

## Think About

- Did I use fragments with style and purpose?
- Did I use informal language when it made sense to do so?
- Does my dialogue sound authentic?
- Did I try weaving in exclamations and single words to add emphasis?

**Preview**

# A Greeting Card Writer

Answer the questions below about the job of a greeting card writer.

1. Greeting cards are everywhere. They may be funny, serious, and everything in between. Imagine you are a writer for a birthday card that a ten-year-old child might receive. What illustrations might you use? What would you say on the front of the card that would make it memorable?

_____

_____

_____

_____

_____

2. What is the best greeting card you've ever received?

_____

_____

_____

_____

_____

3. What writing skills do you think a greeting card writer might need?

_____

_____

_____

_____

_____

# Write-On Sheet

# [ Focus on Conventions ]

Write two sentences that contain correct use of all conventions, including correct verb tenses and subject-verb agreement.

1. _____

_____

_____

2. _____

_____

_____

> 66 You are remembered for the rules you break. 99
>
> —Douglas MacArthur

# [ Greetings to You! ]

How nice of you. My address is 2401 Carrot Drive, Hole #4, Cedar Rabbits, Iowa.

It's your turn to create a greeting card—a thank-you card for someone special. Be creative, innovative, and unique! Almost anything goes, as long as your message is clear and complete.

## Be sure to . . .

✓ Explore a variety of greeting cards to familiarize yourself with different creative approaches, design ideas, and writing styles.

✓ Decide whether to write a humorous or serious card. Think about your purpose, audience, and tone. What kind of reaction do you want the recipient to have?

✓ Brainstorm ideas for your card. Ask yourself, "Why do I want to express my gratitude to this person?"

✓ Think of a short, simple way to express your thoughts and feelings—maybe some bold words, catchy phrases, or a poem. You can use rhyme or regular conversational language. Just keep it heartfelt and easy to follow.

✓ On the front of your card, write a short, catchy lead to get the recipient's attention.

✓ On the inside of the card, complete your message, using only as many words as you need. Make your message powerful, meaningful, and memorable.

✓ Read your card aloud. Does it sound perfect? If not, revise it for sentence fluency.

- **Ideas**
- **Organization**
- **Voice**
- **Word Choice**
- **Sentence Fluency**
- **Conventions**
- **Presentation**

Focus Mode:
Expository

# All Traits

66 The traits give you the language to talk about writing. You've learned a lot about the traits—what they are, how to look for them in your writing, and how to use them when you prewrite, draft, revise, and edit. What makes the traits so great? They help make YOU a great writer! 99

# Putting the Traits Together

All year, you have been breaking down your writing and looking at it trait by trait. Now it's time to look at all five traits at the same time—and see just how far you've come as a writer.

**What do a jigsaw puzzle and a great piece of writing have in common?**

# Circle of Traits

You've been studying Ideas, Organization, Voice, Word Choice, Sentence Fluency, and Conventions all year. Now show what you know! Read the trait names in the pie chart and then highlight or circle the key qualities below in the correct trait color.

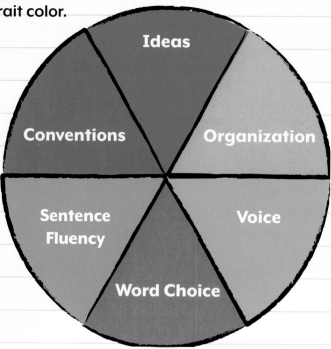

## To write an excellent paper, be sure to . . .

- punctuate effectively
- use sequence and transition words
- create the lead
- end with a sense of resolution
- choose words that deepen meaning
- establish a tone
- create a connection to the audience
- craft well-built sentences

- structure the body
- focus the topic
- apply strong verbs
- break the "rules" to create fluency
- capture smooth and rhythmic flow
- convey the purpose
- apply grammar and usage
- capitalize correctly

- use details
- take risks to create voice
- check spelling
- develop the topic
- select striking words and phrases
- vary sentence types
- use specific and accurate words
- find a topic

# Warm-Up 21

**How well does this writer use all the traits?**

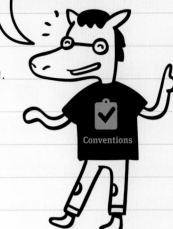

Sentence Fluency with some Organization to go? Delicious!

Conventions

I like pizza. Do you know how to make pizza? Pizza has an interesting history. People all around the world eat pizza. You can put any food on a pizza.

**Revise the paragraph here or on a separate sheet.**

## Think About

- Does my writing show that I understand my topic?
- Are my details in the best possible order?
- Can the reader tell I care about this idea?
- Have I painted a picture with words?
- Does my writing sound good when read aloud?

**Preview**

# Jennifer Berne, author of

## *Manfish: A Story of Jacques Cousteau*

**Find a partner and answer two of the questions below.**

1. Jennifer Berne is the author of *Manfish: A Story of Jacques Cousteau* and *The Boy Who Rode on a Beam of Light: The Story of Albert Einstein.* What kinds of books does she seem to write? Which of her books would you most like to read? Why?

_____

_____

_____

_____

2. *Manfish: A Story of Jacques Cousteau* is about a famous ocean explorer. What would you like to learn about Jacques Cousteau and/or ocean exploration?

_____

_____

_____

_____

3. What famous person's biography, or life story, would you like to read? Why?

_____

_____

_____

_____

# Write-On Sheet

# [ Focus on Conventions ]

Write two sentences that contain correct use of all conventions, including comparative adjectives and adverbs.

1. _____

_____

_____

2. _____

_____

_____

> ❝ We are cups, constantly and quietly being filled. The trick is knowing how to tip ourselves over and let the beautiful stuff out. ❞
>
> **—Ray Bradbury**

# [ Trait Map ]

How does author Jennifer Berne use all the writing traits to explore the remarkable life of oceanographer Jacques Cousteau? Fill in the trait map to critique her work.

# [ Expository Publishing Checklist ]

**Think you are ready to go public with your expository unit project? Use this form to make sure you've covered all the writing bases.**

That wasn't so *ruff*, was it?

**I remembered to**

☐ include facts and information that came from reliable sources.

☐ weave in details that show how much I know about my topic.

☐ develop the topic logically from beginning to end.

☐ use a voice that expresses my fascination for the topic.

☐ explain any unusual words, phrases, or concepts.

☐ read my piece aloud to check how it will sound to the readers.

☐ proofread my piece carefully and clean up problems with conventions.

The purpose of my piece is

_____

_____

The part that works the best is

_____

_____

What I hope readers will take away from my piece is

_____

| Week **1** | Week **2** |
|---|---|
| Reflecting on Myself as a Writer | Saying Good-bye to My Writing Folder |
| Week **3** | Week **4** |
| Celebrating Our Accomplishments | Cleaning Up and Having Fun |

# Wrapping Up the Year

As we roll into the final weeks of the school year, let's look back at what you've learned about the traits and how they've helped you improve your writing. We'll stop and admire what you've written, look ahead to next year, and celebrate your accomplishments—the big ones and the little ones.

# Reflecting on Myself as a Writer

This week, you'll look back at everything you learned this year about being a good writer. You'll investigate one of the traits—what's easy about it, what's hard about it, and how it helped you improve your writing. Then you'll look ahead by writing a letter of introduction to the teacher you've been assigned for next year.

# _____ **Is a Great Trait**

**Use this page to plan your writing trait presentation.**

Trait: _____

Key Qualities:

1. _____

2. _____

3. _____

4. _____

What's so great about this trait:

_____

_____

Favorite book and author that show good use of this trait:

_____

_____

How I would describe the trait to a younger writer:

_____

_____

The best example of this trait from my writing:

_____

_____

# Oral Presentation Checklist

**Use this checklist as you prepare your trait presentation.**

- ☐ What is the symbol or icon that represents this trait?
- ☐ What are this trait's key qualities? Which qualities did I find easy and which were challenging to learn?
- ☐ Can I name an author who applies this trait extremely well in his or her books?
- ☐ Can I share a piece of my writing that improved because I learned something important about this trait?
- ☐ What advice do I have for other writers learning about this trait?

# Letter-Writing Checklist

**Use this list to help you decide what to say in your letter to next year's teacher.**

- ☐ What kind of writing do I enjoy most?
- ☐ What is my greatest strength as a writer?
- ☐ Which trait or step in the writing process do I find challenging?
- ☐ Which trait or step in the writing process do I find easy?
- ☐ What are my personal goals as a writer?
- ☐ What is a favorite book or magazine of mine from this year?
- ☐ What questions do I have for next year's teacher?

# What's Next for Me as a Writer

At the beginning of the year, you set goals for your writing. (See page 11.) Below, briefly assess how well you have met your goals.

_____

_____

_____

Now write three goals you have for next year. Think about how you want to improve as a writer.

Goal 1

_____

_____

_____

Goal 2

_____

_____

_____

Goal 3

_____

_____

_____

# Saying Good-bye to My Writing Folder

Think about all the writing you did this year. You planned, drafted, revised, edited, and published your work. Do you remember the first benchmark paper you turned in? This week you will

1 write a paper in the same mode and on the same topic as that paper, and use the traits to notice improvements you've made in your writing.

2 clean out your writing folder and write a tribute to it.

# Writing a Tribute

A tribute is a statement of thanks or respect to a person, group, or thing. A tribute may

- give examples of specific positive traits of that person, group, or thing.
- contain memories, reflections, quotations, and/or anecdotes.
- explain how the person or thing helped solve problems.
- be written in the form of a speech, poem, song, story, essay, or letter.

This tribute shows how a writing folder helped one student.

I'll never forget the time my Writing Folder helped me power my way through an important debate. I had written what I thought was a pretty persuasive speech for a social studies assignment. At the last minute, I decided to check my Writing Folder for some ideas, and it's a good thing I did. After looking at some of my revisions and notes, I improved the voice. I also reorganized my ending to be more persuasive. Because of those changes, my speech helped my group win the debate. Thank you, Writing Folder.

# Saying Good-bye to My Writing Folder

## My Tribute Planner

Plan the tribute to your writing folder. Use a separate sheet if necessary.

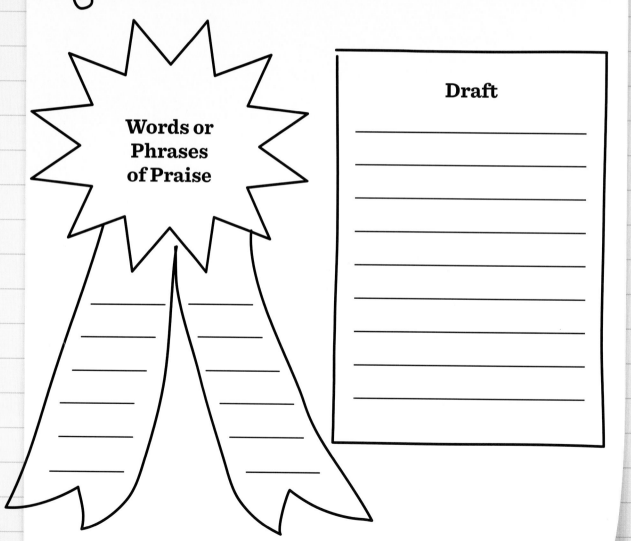

Tribute Format _____

Words or Phrases of Praise

Draft

# Here's to You, My Writing Folder

_(blank lined writing space)_

# Celebrating Our Accomplishments

We celebrate holidays, special events, and now YOU, the writer! Yes, this week you and your classmates will continue wrapping up the writing year. Throw yourselves into the fun activities your teacher has planned for you. It's guaranteed to be a week to remember!

# I'm a HUGE Fan! Planner

**Use this form to help you think through what to write and say to the author.**

The title of the book I liked best this year is

_____

Written by: _____

Illustrated by: _____

I like this author and illustrator because

1. _____

2. _____

3. _____

If I had only one thing to tell the author, I'd want him or her

to know _____

_____

I'd like the illustrator to know _____

_____

How to deliver the letter:

The publisher's address or e-mail is _____

_____

The author or illustrator's website is _____

_____

# Celebrating Our Accomplishments

## Burger Picnic Planner

Plan the menu for your writing picnic. List a food or picnic item for each trait. Think of items related to creating a yummy burger feast.

| Trait | Menu Item |
|---|---|
| **Ideas** | _____ |
| **Organization** | _____ |
| **Voice** | _____ |
| **Word Choice** | _____ |
| **Sentence Fluency** | _____ |
| **Conventions** | _____ |
| **Presentation** | _____ |

What I'd like to bring:

_____.

Why it represents the trait:

_____

_____

_____

# Writing Idol Voting Form

Listen carefully to the pieces that are read each day. Think about the traits and which piece is strongest overall. Record your choices and your explanations. Then, write your choice on a piece of scrap paper and give it to your teacher to tabulate. Shhh...it's a secret ballot!

**Day 1:** My choice for Writing Idol finalist is

_____

because _____.

**Day 2:** My choice for Writing Idol finalist is

_____

because _____.

**Day 3:** My choice for Writing Idol finalist is

_____

because _____.

**Day 4:** My choice for Writing Idol finalist is

_____

because _____.

**Day 5:** I choose _____ as our class Writing Idol for the year because

_____

_____

_____.

# Cleaning Up and Having Fun

This is it—the last writing week. You'll clean up your space (including gym socks!) and help your teacher tidy up the classroom, too. You might win the coveted "Tidy to the Max" award! You'll play some writing-related games and have some fun with words and language. It's time to have some final good times together and say so long!

# Writing in Code

Use a substitution code to create a secret good-bye message. For each letter of the alphabet, substitute another letter. Then use your code to write the message in the grid, one letter per block. (Don't forget to leave an empty block between words.)

| A | B | C | D | E | F | G | H | I | J | K | L | M |
|---|---|---|---|---|---|---|---|---|---|---|---|---|
|   |   |   |   |   |   |   |   |   |   |   |   |   |

| N | O | P | Q | R | S | T | U | V | W | X | Y | Z |
|---|---|---|---|---|---|---|---|---|---|---|---|---|
|   |   |   |   |   |   |   |   |   |   |   |   |   |

# Ideas

**the content of your piece—its central message and the details that support that message**

**6 EXPERT**

**HIGH**

My topic is well developed and focused. My piece contains specific, interesting, and accurate details, and new thinking about this topic.

- I have a clear central theme or a simple, original story line.
- I've narrowed my theme or story line to create a focused piece that is a pleasure to read.
- I've included original information to support my main idea.
- I've included specific, interesting, and accurate details that will create pictures in the reader's mind.

**5 WELL DONE**

**4 ALMOST THERE**

**MIDDLE**

My piece includes many general observations about the topic, but lacks focus and clear, accurate details. I need to elaborate.

- I've stayed on the topic, but my theme or story line is too broad.
- I haven't dug into the topic in a logical, focused way.
- My unique perspective on this topic is not coming through as clearly as it could.
- The reader may have questions after reading this piece because my details leave some questions unanswered.

**3 MAKING STRIDES**

**2 ON MY WAY**

**LOW**

I'm still thinking about the theme or story line for this piece. So far, I've only explored possibilities.

- I've jotted down some ideas for topics, but it's a hodgepodge.
- Nothing in particular stands out as important in my piece.
- I have not written much. I may have only restated the assignment.
- My details are thin and need to be checked for accuracy.

**1 GETTING STARTED**

# Organization

the internal structure of your piece—the thread of logic, the pattern of meaning

**6 EXPERT**

My details unfold in a logical order. The structure makes reading my piece a breeze.

- My beginning grabs the reader's attention.
- I've used sequence and transition words to guide the reader.
- All of my details fit together logically and move along smoothly.
- My ending gives the reader a sense of closure and something to think about.

**HIGH**

**5 WELL DONE**

**4 ALMOST THERE**

My piece's organization is pretty basic and predictable. I have the three essential ingredients, a beginning, middle, and end, but that's about it.

- My beginning is clear, but unoriginal. I've used a technique that writers use all too often.
- I've used simple sequence and transition words that stand out too much.
- Details need to be added or moved around to create a more logical flow of ideas.
- My ending needs work; it's pretty canned.

**MIDDLE**

**3 MAKING STRIDES**

**2 ON MY WAY**

My piece doesn't make much sense because I haven't figured out a way to organize it. The details are jumbled together at this point.

- My beginning doesn't indicate where I'm going or why I'm going there.
- I have not grouped ideas or connected them using sequence and transition words.
- With no sense of order, it will be a challenge for the reader to sort out how the details relate.
- I haven't figured out how to end this piece.

**LOW**

**1 GETTING STARTED**

# Voice

**the tone of the piece—your personal stamp, which is achieved through an understanding of purpose and audience**

### 6 EXPERT

**HIGH**

I've come up with my own "take" on the topic. I had my audience and purpose clearly in mind as I wrote and presented my ideas in an original way.

- My piece is expressive, which shows how much I care about my topic.
- The purpose for this piece is clear, and I've used a tone that suits that purpose.
- There is no doubt in my mind that the reader will understand how I think and feel about my topic.
- I've expressed myself in some new, original ways.

### 5 WELL DONE

### 4 ALMOST THERE

**MIDDLE**

My feelings about the topic come across as uninspired and predictable. The piece is not all that expressive, nor does it reveal a commitment to the topic.

- In a few places, my authentic voice comes through, but only in a few.
- My purpose for writing this piece is unclear to me, so the tone feels "off."
- I've made little effort to connect with the reader; I'm playing it safe.
- This piece sounds like lots of others on this topic. It's not very original.

### 3 MAKING STRIDES

### 2 ON MY WAY

**LOW**

I haven't thought at all about my purpose or audience for the piece and, therefore, my voice falls flat. I'm pretty indifferent to the topic and it shows.

- I've put no energy into this piece.
- My purpose for writing this piece is a mystery to me, so I'm casting about aimlessly.
- Since my topic isn't interesting to me, chances are my piece won't be interesting to the reader. I haven't thought about my audience.
- I have taken no risks. There is no evidence that I find this topic interesting or care about it at all.

### 1 GETTING STARTED

# Word Choice

### the vocabulary you use to convey meaning and enlighten the reader

**6 EXPERT**

**HIGH**

The words and phrases I've selected are accurate, specific, and natural-sounding. My piece conveys precisely what I want to say, because of my powerful vocabulary.

- My piece contains strong verbs that bring it alive.
- I stretched by using the perfect words and phrases to convey my ideas.
- I've used content words and phrases with accuracy and precision.
- I've picked the best words and phrases, not just the first ones that came to mind.

**5 WELL DONE**

**4 ALMOST THERE**

**MIDDLE**

My words and phrases make sense but aren't very accurate, specific, or natural-sounding. The reader won't have trouble understanding them. However, he or she may find them uninspiring.

- I've used passive voice. I should rethink passages that contain passive voice and add "action words."
- I haven't come up with extraordinary ways to say ordinary things.
- My content words and phrases are accurate but general. I might have overused jargon. I need to choose words that are more precise.
- I need to revise this piece by replacing its weak words and phrases with strong ones.

**3 MAKING STRIDES**

**2 ON MY WAY**

**LOW**

My words and phrases are so unclear the reader may wind up more confused than entertained, informed, or persuaded. I need to expand my vocabulary to improve this piece.

- My verbs are not strong. Passive voice permeates this piece.
- I've used bland words and phrases throughout—or the same words and phrases over and over.
- My content words are neither specific nor accurate enough to make the meaning clear.
- My words and phrases are not working; they distract the reader rather than guide him or her.

**1 GETTING STARTED**

# Sentence Fluency

**the way the text looks and sounds as it flows through your piece**

**6 EXPERT**

**HIGH**

My piece is strong because I've written a variety of well-built sentences. I've woven those sentences together to create a smooth-sounding piece.

- I've constructed and connected my sentences for maximum impact.
- I've varied my sentence lengths and types—short and long, simple and complex.
- When I read my piece aloud, it is pleasing to my ear.
- I've broken grammar rules intentionally at points to create impact and interest.

**5 WELL DONE**

**4 ALMOST THERE**

**MIDDLE**

Although my sentences lack variety or creativity, most of them are grammatically correct. Some of them are smooth, while others are choppy and awkward.

- I've written solid shorter sentences. Now I need to try some longer ones.
- I've created different kinds of sentences, but the result is uneven.
- When I read my piece aloud, I stumble in a few places.
- Any sentences that break grammar rules are accidental and don't work well.

**3 MAKING STRIDES**

**2 ON MY WAY**

**LOW**

My sentences are choppy, incomplete, or rambling. I need to revise my piece extensively to make it more readable.

- Many of my sentences don't work because they're poorly constructed.
- I've used the same sentence lengths and types over and over again.
- When I read my piece aloud, I stumble in many places.
- If I've broken grammar rules, it's not for stylistic reasons—it's because I may not understand those rules.

**1 GETTING STARTED**

# Conventions

**the mechanical correctness of your piece, which helps guide the reader through the text**

## 6 EXPERT

My piece proves I can use a range of conventions with skill and creativity. It is ready for its intended audience.

- My spelling is strong. I've spelled all or nearly all the words accurately.
- I've used punctuation creatively and correctly and have begun new paragraphs in the right places.
- I've used capital letters correctly throughout my piece, even in tricky places.
- I've taken care to apply standard English grammar and usage.

**HIGH**

## 5 WELL DONE

## 4 ALMOST THERE

My writing still needs editing to correct problems in one or more conventions. I've stuck to the basics and haven't tried challenging conventions.

- I've misspelled words that I use all the time, as well as complex words that I don't use as often.
- My punctuation is basically strong, but I should review it one more time. I indented some of the paragraphs, but not all of them.
- I've correctly used capital letters in obvious places (such as the word *I*) but not in others.
- Even though my grammar and usage are not 100 percent correct, my audience should be able to read my piece.

**MIDDLE**

## 3 MAKING STRIDES

## 2 ON MY WAY

The problems I'm having with conventions make this piece challenging to read, even for me! I've got lots of work to do before it's ready for its intended audience.

- Extensive spelling errors make my piece difficult to read and understand.
- I haven't punctuated or paragraphed the piece well, which makes it difficult for the reader to understand or enjoy my writing.
- My use of capital letters is so inconsistent it's distracting.
- I need to clean up the piece considerably in terms of grammar and usage.

**LOW**

## 1 GETTING STARTED

# Presentation

the physical appearance of your piece—the welcome mat that invites the reader in

## 6 EXPERT

**HIGH**

My piece's appearance makes it easy to read and enjoy. I've taken care to ensure that it is pleasing to my reader's eye.

- I've written clearly and legibly. My letters, words, and the spaces between them are uniform.
- My choice of font style, size, and/or color makes my piece a breeze to read.
- My margins frame the text nicely. There are no tears, smudges, or cross-outs.
- Text features such as bulleted lists, charts, pictures, and headers are working well.

## 5 WELL DONE

## 4 ALMOST THERE

**MIDDLE**

My piece still looks like a draft. Many visual elements should be cleaned up and handled with more care.

- My handwriting is readable, but my letters and words and the spaces between them should be treated more consistently.
- My choice of font style, size, and/or color seems "off"—inappropriate for my intended audience.
- My margins are uneven. There are some tears, smudges, or cross-outs.
- I've handled simple text features well but am struggling with the more complex ones.

## 3 MAKING STRIDES

## 2 ON MY WAY

**LOW**

My piece is almost unreadable because of its appearance. It's not ready for anyone but me to read.

- My handwriting is so hard to read it creates a visual barrier.
- The font styles, sizes, and/or colors I've chosen are dizzying. They're not working.
- My margins are uneven or nonexistent, making the piece difficult to read.
- I haven't used text features well, even simple ones.

## 1 GETTING STARTED